heartbeats
of hope

The Empowerment Way
to Recover Your Life

Daniel Fisher, MD, PhD

National
EMPOWERMENT
Center, Inc.

LAWRENCE, MASSACHUSETTS

ISBN : 978-0-692-76459-6

This edition published by the National Empowerment Center, Inc.
599 Canal St., Lawrence, MA 01840
1-800-POWER2U
1-978-685-1494
www.power2u.org

Design and typesetting by Jane Tenenbaum
Cover design by Kim Smith
Illustrations by author, Kimberly Smith, Currier and Ives,
Lark Fisher, and Sabine Tibbetts

Printed by Park Printing

The 1997 South African Governmental White Paper on Social Welfare officially recognized *ubuntu* as:

> *The principle of caring for each other's well-being . . . and a spirit of mutual support . . . Each individual's humanity is ideally expressed through his or her relationship with others and theirs in turn through a recognition of the individual's humanity. Ubuntu means that people are people through other people. It also acknowledges both the rights and the responsibilities of every citizen in promoting individual and societal well-being.*

DEDICATION

I lovingly dedicate this book to my wife, Tish, my daughters Lauren and Caitlin, and my extended family, friends, and allies who have inspired and supported me through this journey called life.

CONTENTS

heartbeats of hope

At times I feel frightened

Dark, cold, and alone

My heart misses beats

leaves fall,

Death's icy breath

Chills my neck.

What is the use?

Only a cliff ahead,

Life interrupted.

But a smile

a touch,

a hug, can

Light a fire,

Blow upon

a forgotten ember

Bring warmth,

Restore the flow of my heart

Chase heartspasms of fear

With heartbeats of hope

SUMMARY OF THE CHAPTERS

PART I

Chapter One describes my life until age twenty-four. I call this period my "mockingbird" phase during which I believed there was one cohesive version of reality, a monologue constructed by authorities, to which I strove to comply.

Chapter Two explores my life-changing years from age twenty-four to thirty, which I call my raven period. During this time I discovered my own unique Voice, and began to engage in dialogue with the world. I experienced several periods of extreme emotional states labeled psychosis, which helped me to integrate my deeper Self.

In **Chapter Three**, my life takes flight, like a great blue heron. I learn to recover a full life in the community, by using my Voice in collaborating with a variety of others' perspectives. By doing so I achieved more of a symphony of Voices.

PART II

Chapter Four is a summary of all the lessons I have learned through recovering my life in the community.

Chapter Five summarizes my thoughts at this time about the development of my Self. I also describe the National Empowerment Center's "Empowerment Paradigm of Recovery, Healing, and Development" as an alternative to the medical model of illness.

PART III

In **Chapter Six**, I propose a synthesis of the recovery vision developed by peers with the Open Dialogue approach developed by clinicians. I call this synthesis of recovery and Open Dialogue, Dialogical Recovery of Life.

In **Chapter Seven**, I discuss the importance of each peer finding their Voice, and provide a resource for guiding peers to reclaim their Voice so that they can engage in passionate dialogue with others from their community and with those outside their community.

Chapter Eight describes Emotional CPR (eCPR), a peer-designed training program, which teaches anyone how to help support a person through an emotional crisis, without the use of diagnostic labels or coercive treatment.

In **Chapter Nine**, I introduce Recovery Dialogues, a series of meetings where peers and providers can use the principles of dialogue to weave recovery practices into the culture of the conventional mental health system.

Chapter Ten focuses on the origin and practice of Open Dialogue. I give an example of how I use it in my own therapy practice in Massachusetts.

In **Chapter Eleven**, I summarize what I understand about recovery of life, and look to a time when everyone who experiences mental health challenges will be able to live a meaningful life in the community of their choice.

A WORD ABOUT TERMS

When I refer to **community**, I mean free life outside of institutions.

Consumers are people presently receiving services. **Psychiatric survivors** are those who are out of the system and feel they survived the system. **Ex-patient** was an early term to designate that we were no longer patients. Some of us now refer to ourselves as **persons with lived experience of recovery**. Overall, though, we prefer to be called people, just like everyone else.

The term **peer** means a person who has shared the experience of having a mental health condition and who often provides support in the system. **Peer advocates** and **peer supporters** are other names.

I use **Self** with a capital **S** to distinguish the true Self from a person's lowercase "self" — their false self — per the language of R. D. Laing in his book *The Divided Self.*

I capitalize **Voice** when I am referring to the unique expression of who we truly are. I think of Voice with a capital **V** as the expression of one's true Self. I hope that this book is an expression of my Voice.

My transformation from isolated scientist to humanitarian

INTRODUCTION

Why did I write this book? In the beginning, I wrote this book to show that I recovered from what is labeled by the mental health system as schizophrenia. I wrote the book to give hope to others labeled with schizophrenia or other severe psychiatric diagnoses. In the course of writing and living, however, I discovered that the lessons I and others learned in our recovery from what are described as "mental health conditions" can help everyone lead fuller, more meaningful lives. You will see that I emphasize the universal aspects of living rather than describing life in terms of labels and symptoms. Indeed, an essential aspect of recovery from severe emotional states is to understand that they are not mental illnesses but are important opportunities for growth and development.

I have discovered that there is a dimension of being beyond words that is the fire of life. When the sparks of our being are nearly extinguished, others are invaluable in their restoration. When I was a young man, I thought words and thoughts were the most important aspect of life. "I think, therefore I am," was my philosophy. People were merely a means to achieve deeper thoughts. Thank heavens I broke down and broke through the cocoon in which I had wrapped myself. I have now learned that I had the idea of living upside down: I should have been saying, "I am, therefore I can think" and "I relate, therefore I am."

On three occasions between age twenty-four to thirty, I stopped living. I was still breathing but my deepest Self threw the switch of my existence from "maybe I want to live" to "no, I do not want to live." I still recall tracking down the last ember of my life inside and trying to choke it off. My life lost all meaning. I lost my will to go on living because I was not really living anyway. I didn't actively take my own life but simply stopped every outward sign of life: I stopped talking, eating, and moving. The authorities call it catatonic schizophrenia. I call it losing my will to live and withdrawing so deep inside that only the most persistent people could find me.

This book is about how I went from saying "no" to life to saying "yes" to life. I recovered by learning the language of my heartbeats — the heartbeats of my emotions and my life. I now believe that it is our heartbeats that carry us through the frightening spaces of life. I thought and thought and my heart stopped talking to me. A friend said it so well recently: "Our words and thoughts can be an interruption, but our heart flows."

I recall experiencing the terror of being alone as a small child. One such searing memory was of being put on a train to go to sleep-away camp for two months when I was ten. As my parents were putting me on the train, they suddenly realized they had not gotten me a train ticket. They ran towards the ticket counter, yelling, "We will be right back." But the train pulled out of Baltimore station before they could get back. I panicked. What would I do on the train with no ticket? Surely the conductor would throw me off into the weeds I saw quickly passing by. I didn't know I was on a "camp car" with a counselor who would make sure I had a ticket. Only later did I realize the way in which my life was interrupted by not being able to say goodbye to my parents. Throughout my life, loss of love has been the trigger for severe distress.

The following drawing illustrates the theme of this book. When I was twenty-four, my wife left and I was devastated. I withdrew into my own world, a world of monologue. I had a broken heart and felt I was disappearing. Then through very important relationships, like the figures on the right, I was able to engage in emotional dialogue with others and myself at the heart and mind levels. That emotional dialogue has been essential to my recovery and growth of life.

For me, recovery is about opening up to relationships, being open to love and wonder with others, and being open to one's Self. I am shocked to see that just as I have been waking up to this reality, the world around me appears to be heading down a perilous path. Just as I am discovering the importance of intimate, loving relationships, our society is becoming convinced that emotional distress is due to impersonal chemical imbalances. Just when a number of us have discovered the vital power of sharing our personal experiences of hope and recovery, society has focused on medication as the primary relief for psychological pain. Just when we are learning that our emotional distress originates from loss of connection with others and ourselves,

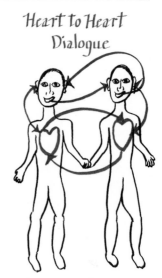

society is convinced that our distress is a mental *illness*. As Dr. Thomas Szasz wrote fifty-six years ago, there cannot be mental illness. Our minds are a process, not a structure, and depend on our connections with others. Our minds are nourished by dialogue between a genuine *I* and a genuine *you*. Our minds cannot be reduced simply to the material aspect of our brain. A process cannot be an illness in the usual sense. The act of reducing our minds to molecules is deadening—and traumatic. This reduction is turning human beings into robotic objects and is killing us.

Many people conclude, incorrectly, that my emphasis on the emotional and social dimensions of psychosis mean that I am opposed to medication. I am not anti-medication; I am for humane alternatives to medication. In fact, I am a board-certified psychiatrist and I prescribe psychiatric medication when other approaches alone fail to facilitate recovery. I give the lowest possible dose for the shortest time they seem needed. I always tell the person for whom I prescribe medication, and their supporters, that the medication will only assist them in accessing their own capacity to connect, heal, and recover their life. I always want the person to be an active participant in their own recovery.

Personally, there were times during my recovery when people could not reach me or I could not reach myself. At those times, the major tranquilizers they gave me may have helped. However, I never stayed on them for more than a few months after hospitalization and switched to an "as-needed basis." I have been off all psychiatric medications for more than 40 years. I am not an exception in being able to live a full life without medication after several psychotic periods. A recent study led by Dr. Wunderink in the Netherlands, has also found that being diagnosed with schizophrenia does not mean one must be on medication for a lifetime. In fact, the study found that the group that was withdrawn from antipsychotic medication was more likely to recover than the group kept on medication continuously over a seven-year period.

It is time to wake up the world to these realities before it is too late. It is time to demonstrate the need for and effectiveness of providing more interpersonal resources for mental health. We must act before our society is so medicated that it cannot feel the pain that it must experience in order to take action and reach out. Those of us who suffer consider ourselves emotional canaries in an emotionally toxic society. Just as coal miners carried canaries into underground shafts as a primitive warning mechanism against exposure to poisonous fumes, we act as society's emotional canaries, endangered by the toxic, impersonal ways of our modern world. We must all avoid being like Emily in Thornton Wilder's play *Our Town*. Upon viewing the brief span of her life from the perspective of the grave, Emily reflects that, "Life goes by so fast, we barely have time to look at each other."

I have been fortunate enough to recover from what was diagnosed as schizophrenia. In fact, many other people have also recovered. I now see my journey as a gift to myself and to society. Rather than being viewed as outcasts to be despised, those of us who have recovered from supposedly permanent "mental illnesses," should be viewed as resources. In some countries, we are called shamans and are valued for our help rather than rejected or ignored.

It is important for the world to know that there is always hope for recovery. It is equally important for the world to know that the manner in which people are treated is crucial to that recovery. I am furious that many people in positions of power try to convince the public that there is no hope for persons diagnosed with schizophrenia and other severe emotional conditions. These charlatans are often richly rewarded because their teachings perpetuate the status quo.

The frequently stated belief that individual genetic factors are the primary cause for human behavior promotes a dangerous supposition: that people are unable to improve their station in life. The proponents of these ideas attempt to repudiate those of us who have recovered. This discrimination, and their predictions of doom, also prevent our society from investing in resources to address the social causes behind our mental health issues.

My book begins with the story of my own journey of recovery through self-acceptance and self-understanding. I discuss my view of what recovery looks like, supplemented with additional evidence that people *can* recover. I then share some ideas about how recovery occurs, including the "empowerment paradigm of recovery." Finally, I recommend ways to implement this recovery approach in daily life through Emotional CPR (eCPR).

In December 2009, I received an email from Suzanne. She contacted me after the loss of her son a year-and-a-half earlier. In that email, she described how she wanted to create an alternative healing center dedicated to demonstrating that the National Empowerment Center's empowerment paradigm of recovery could help young people recover from psychosis. "I'm long on hope and short on confidence," she wrote. "Although I have a passion and a vision, I am relatively powerless. I am just a heartbroken mother who lost her son to madness and desperately wants to change the status quo. I so agree with you that it's time for total transformation of treatment for those in severe emotional distress."

Her letter pierced my heart. I replied, "Your passion will light the way. I read your email with sadness and outrage. I am so sorry that you lost your son. Though I survived my spirit-breaking experiences in hospitals, my passion for change is fueled by dreams from people like you. We desperately need alternatives to hospitals, alternatives to hopelessness, alternatives to a medication-only approach." Several years later I helped start such an alternative in Massachusetts, which is called a "peer-run respite." Peer-run respites are small, home-like settings run by people with lived experience that offer an alternative to psychiatric hospitalization.

I learned that Suzanne's gifted and artistic son, Jake, had developed severe mental health issues, had became homeless, and had been killed when hit by an Amtrak train while crossing the tracks in Santa Barbara, California. Suzanne and Jake's story struck such a chord in me that it motivated me to forge my writings of thirty years into this book. Suzanne agreed to use our dialogue as the motivation. She thought it important to get the word out that people can and do recover from madness. "My vision for this book," she said, "is that it be a gorgeous house of hope."

I am brought to tears when I think of Jake. I watched Suzanne give a moving TED* talk in which she made a plea to end the lies about mental health issues. In it, she showed pictures of Jake laughing, growing, living, creating, and then having his hope taken away. As I listened, I recalled my own feeling of hopelessness when I was diagnosed with schizophrenia and the deadening feeling of being on major tranquilizers. I also recalled the life-long struggle my sister Lark has had with her own mental health issues. Slowly my sadness has been replaced by passionate outrage. How can so many people be wrong? How can the experts be so misguided?

When I was young I repressed my emotions; I believed they interfered with pure thought. I was also afraid to express my emotions because I didn't want to get into conflicts. Now I treasure my emotions. It's important to me that I feel outrage when I hear of Jake. When I cry, I feel the oneness of my mind and my body, my past and my present, my pain and my joy. My tears make me feel whole and vital; they connect me to Jake, Suzanne, and Lark.

This morning, I sang "Over the Rainbow" to feel why the song seemed so important to me. As I sang, I saw my sister as a bird flying free of her pain. I saw Jake beside her flying free of his pain and all the thousands of lost souls who, as Lark once wrote, "Wander this weary, watery world." Tears are running down my cheek as I write this. I feel the intensity with which I have been trying to heal my dear beloved

---

*TED is a global community, welcoming people from every discipline and culture who seek a deeper understanding of the world, and sponsors short talks to bring forth new ideas.

sister. I allow myself to feel the remorse I experience because I could recover but she could not. It seems that one reason I drove myself to the depths of psychosis was to find a way out for her. I am reminded of my first hospitalization in Johns Hopkins Hospital. I am looking at the walls of the seclusion room. There are drawings on the wall. I examine them closely and am convinced that my sister had drawn them because she had been in there before me. In fact, though she had been hospitalized before me, it was at another hospital.

I want this book to be about hope. We will build a ship of hope among the fragments of our lives. The spirit of that hope wells up in every word I call forth. I recognize Emily Dickinson's bird of hope in a relentless storm:

Hope is the thing with feathers —
That perches in the soul —
And sings the tune without the words —
And never stops — at all —

Dickinson points out that hope dwells in the soul and sings a wordless tune that never stops. The image of it having feathers is one of wings; hope is like a bird that carries our soul to freedom through flight. The singing reminds me of the importance of having our own Voice. That the singing never stops points to the importance of persistence even in dark times. A similar theme was shared by the mystic Master Ekhardt: "The soul has something in it, a spark *(funklein)* of speech *(redelicheit)* that never dies...the soul's spark, which is untouched by space and time."

Hope is always cited as a vital aspect of recovery, and yet it is poorly understood. Without it recovery cannot begin or proceed. Without hope there can be no life. Yet, what inspires hope? When hope is in short supply it seems we must borrow it from others. But how does that work? Suzanne's plaintive call was a cry for hope. If only she and Jake had known that people could recover from schizophrenia, he might have lived. Hopelessness is cited as the most serious risk factor for suicide. She and others have told me that a vital reason for my telling my own story of recovery is to give hope. They say that my story counters the myth that people do not recover. If this book can give hope to one person I will have had a reason to write it.

Several years ago, I traveled to Japan for a speaking engagement. A professor of nursing had also traveled a great distance from Okinawa to Tokyo to hear me. When I asked her what brought her to the talk, she told me, "In the past I had only read in textbooks that people can never recover from schizophrenia and other forms of severe mental distress. Then I read the story of your recovery on a website. This gave me renewed hope. I want to hear you speak of your recovery first-hand, so I can carry that hope in my heart — back to the students that I teach."

My recovery from schizophrenia has been fueled by the evolution of my spirit, my Voice, and my sense that my life is worth living. In writing this, I am overcoming the negative voices that tell me, "You are not capable. You have nothing unique to offer. The answers are written already." I am inspired by a quotation from Martin Luther King, Jr.:

> *Forces that threaten to negate life must be challenged by courage, which is the power of life, to affirm itself in spite of life's ambiguities. This requires the exercise of creative will that enables us to hew out a stone of hope from a mountain of despair.*

I hope that this book brings hope into your heart and enables you to hew your stone of hope, too. Then you, too, will hear heartbeats of hope, as I do.

Recovery Is Possible for Everyone When We Experience Our Shared Humanity

Recovery is not just the activity of a few of us who have been diagnosed with major mental health issues. We who have recovered have been building a movement of alternatives to the traditional mental health system because that system has failed to address the community-wide issues we are reacting to. As Australians say, "I cannot be healthy if my community is not healthy, and my community cannot be healthy unless I am healthy."

Today our mental health system focuses on relieving a person's symptoms, but it does not help people heal the deeper human wounds we all share. In this sense, the mental health system itself is merely treating society's symptoms without questioning its deeper issues. The Occupy Movement (2011–present) has highlighted these deeper issues. In many ways, we have been colonized by an industrial, mechanical mode of thinking. Our lives belong to corporations, not to ourselves. We are all in the matrix of machinery and computers. Therefore, we all need to occupy our own lives and throw off this colonized way of being. Though a deeper analysis of these economic and political forces are beyond the scope of this book they are reflected in the major themes I will discuss.

The themes of this book are:

- Our natural drive is to become whole human beings living a full life in a community, connected at a heart-to-heart level to those around us.
- When this natural drive to become whole is thwarted by trauma, we experience distress, which is interpreted as symptoms of mental illness. In actuality, this distress is an attempt to become more fully human.
- The present mental health system is interfering with recovery by dehumanizing people and robbing them of hope and their rights; medications are overused and authentic relationships are underused.
- There is always hope that everyone can recover their humanity.
- When people in distress form heart-to-heart connections with others they can connect with their own heart and recover their humanity.
- We can only reach the deepest Self of another person in distress when we are also able to engage in emotional dialogue with our deepest Self.
- Emotional dialogue is best engaged in by persons who have their own lived experience of recovery of life.
- Recovery of our humanity best occurs in communities of persons with shared values of love and mutual respect.
- We need to create economic, educational, and social structures based upon sharing the love and mutual respect needed to recover our shared humanity.

PART I

Recovering My Life

My journey to find my humanity unfolded in three phases.
During the first phase of my life, until I was twenty-four, I lived
like a mockingbird. I was asleep in one version of the world, which
was my monologue. It was the narrative of the world that was given
to me by authorities. I found it difficult being me. I mistrusted myself.
I needed to fulfill my family's expectations of who I was meant to
be. My emotional needs were secondary. I was to become the sixth
generation in my family to be a doctor. I was nicknamed by my father,
"The Golden Boy." I had achieved external success by age twenty-four:
I was married and had earned a PhD in biochemistry. However, I felt
empty inside. I had no voice of my own and no sense of my own self.

In the second phase of my life, from age twenty-four to thirty, I
was melancholy, like Edgar Allen Poe's raven. I was waking up through
dialogue with a very different world around me. My life-changing experience started the day my wife left. I was devastated and felt that
my life was no longer worth living. Like the raven, I was mourning
for my lost love. Painful though it was, I am now grateful that she left
because, by doing so, she forced me to find my authentic Voice and
stop being a mockingbird. I was diagnosed with schizophrenia and
broke through the mask I had constructed. I had to break through in
order to recover my life by uncovering my true Self.

In the third phase of my journey, from age thirty to the present, I
am developing my authentic Self to be an involved and loving person.

In this phase, I see myself as a great blue heron. I am part of the flock of humanity, gracefully living in harmony with the world. This is the period during which I found meaningful love and work. This is the story of my journey from fear to love. I am integrating the varied voices and versions of reality within and around me.

ONE

Existing for Others

I was born in Towson, Maryland, and lived on a street called Terrace Dale. The house was on a hill overlooking a highway, the York Road. I lived there with my sister Sally, who is nine years older, and my brother Sandy who is four years older. My father was a doctor. My mother was responsible of taking care of the children. My memories of that house are pleasant. I felt we were part of a community and our family seemed happy.

There was a family story about how I had nearly died when I was a year old. As a child I was confused about the details but it was so important that when I was older, I told any new kids about the event. As I would display the scar on my neck, I would then tell them that when I was a baby I had a very severe case of pneumonia. I would tell them that I was dying and that my father had saved my life by cutting open my throat and enabling me to breathe.

In actuality, this turned out to be the fusing of two separate stories: my own and that of an ancestor. In reality, when I was only a year old, I contracted croup and I had to be hospitalized. I couldn't breathe and a pediatrician performed a tracheotomy. I also developed pneumonia and was placed in an oxygen tent. In 1944, when this occurred, doctors only used 1,000 units of penicillin each day to combat infections. At the time, my father had been working with a team of researchers at Johns Hopkins Hospital to improve the effectiveness of penicillin. His research revealed that animals could tolerate ten times the dose used at that time. So he recommended that my dose of penicillin be increased to 10,000 units. I got better — and from then on my mother never argued with my father about his research causing him to be late to dinner. So my father did indeed save my life, though through his research rather than by performing a tracheotomy.

The other tracheotomy story had happened seventy years earlier. My great-grandfather, Frank LeMoyne, was also a doctor. He had a six-year-old daughter, Manette, who developed diphtheria. He performed a tracheotomy on her at home because the diphtheria had closed her windpipe. The story was that he cried as he performed the tracheotomy on Manette. She dried his tears and said, "There, there, Father, I will be all right." She died soon after she uttered those words. The LeMoyne family had a particularly large influence on my life because two of my great-grandfathers were LeMoyne brothers: Frank and John (my parents were second cousins).

I must have had a strong independent streak. According to my mother, when I was two, I suddenly took off for the York Road, much to her horror. Apparently a truck driver stopped, picked me up, and carried me back to the front yard. Another dramatic moment was the night a streetcar on York Road struck the car in which my mother and sister were traveling. They were mildly injured but the shock of it persisted.

When I was three, we moved to a small, red-brick house in the upscale town of Ruxton. The house had been built by my father's diminutive cousin, Mac Fisher. As we entered the door for the first time my six-foot-three father said, "A nice little house for little Mac." During this part of my childhood, my mother was often asking questions of herself and of me. Perhaps this is the reason why I keep searching for deeper truths. My father told me stories of his childhood and he demonstrated to me his caring approach toward his patients when I accompanied him on his rounds at Johns Hopkins Hospital.

I attended Gilman School where I felt a sense of place and continuity. Only later did I learn that it was founded fifty years earlier by my great-grandfather Fisher. I spent twelve years there. Though at times it seemed oppressive, I think it helped me forge a great inner strength. I have always sensed that during the darkest times there is a part of me inside that I draw upon. I think that this sense of Self was the result of being nurtured by caring parents and a supportive community during my early years.

I was the peacemaker in my family. At times there were painful fights, arguments, and tears at my house. My brother fought with my older sister; my brother fought with me; my mother and father argued over money. I said to myself, "I am not going to cause them any trouble; they already have too much trouble. I am going to be quiet, reasonable, and helpful." I would always look for a way to help people get along.

Ruxton's small town roots anchored me. I fondly recall the personal contacts and sense of belonging during the late '40s and early '50s. I remember singing Christmas carols in community gatherings. We picked up our mail each day at the post office where Mrs. Potts, the postmistress, filled us in on the latest town news and gossip. Her son ran the gas station and our neighbors ran the grocery store. The milkman delivered dairy goods and good stories. Even having operator assisted telephone calls seemed reassuring as you could also ask the operator for the time and the weather forecast. I had a sense of belonging through my father's family. There were many Fishers in Ruxton and they had contributed positively to the life of the community as doctors, engineers, and lawyers. My father was my hero and still is.

The life of my great-great-grandfather Francis Julius LeMoyne was an additional inspiration. He was known as a fearless advocate of the oppressed and of those in need. In addition to being a doctor, he was an abolitionist whose house in Washington, Pennsylvania was part of the Underground Railroad. I have a document dated 1837 on which his signature appears along with other prominent local citizens of the day petitioning the country to end slavery. His father, a doctor, and his father-in-law, a lawyer, emigrated from France in 1790 to avoid the excesses of the French Revolution. They settled in Gallipolis, Ohio.

I was very close — perhaps too close — to my mother. I can clearly recall sitting on her lap while she wore a checked tweed suit. She held me tight and said, "You are my little boy, and you always will be." I would at times comb her hair, parting it carefully down the middle. I also would notice the scar from the auto accident with the streetcar on York Road. One of my last joyful memories was the morning of my fourth birthday. I ran into my parents' bedroom and dove onto their bed. They had hidden presents under the covers, one of which was a red fire engine. Shortly after that, I sat for a pastel portrait, which hung in my mother's bedroom until she died sixty-four years later. In it, I am holding the fire engine and seem to be smiling contentedly.

I was a quiet, shy, and sensitive boy by nature. My favorite book was *The Story of Ferdinand* by Munro Leaf. The story began, "Once upon a time in Spain, there was a little bull and his name was Ferdinand. All the other bulls he lived with would run and jump and butt their heads together, but not Ferdinand. He liked to just sit quietly and smell the flowers..." Ferdinand grows up to be very strong, but still prefers to smell the flowers under his favorite cork tree. His mother worries that not butting heads with the other young bulls will leave him lonely, but he says he is happier being alone and smelling the flowers. One day he is stung by a bee while men are picking the best bull for a bullfight. Off he is hauled to the bullring. Once there he refuses to fight and is sent back home to sit out his days under his cork tree. I identified with Ferdinand. I had a baby doll that I loved to feed and clothe—yet I would later become a wrestler. Only now do I realize what a conflict that must have caused inside me.

Three months after my fourth birthday, my younger sister Lark was born and I experienced an acute loss of my mother's attention. Every child has difficulty adjusting to the birth of the next sibling, but in my case the loss seemed particularly painful because of my mother's reaction to Lark's birth. Though her condition was not diagnosed at the time, my mother seems to have descended into a severe post-partum depression. In fact, it seems she remained depressed for the next twenty years. She likened the experience of having her fourth child (Lark, fourteen years after her first) to drowning. She also wrote in her journal how sorry she felt for me: "I am sad to see that Dan's crown is slipping."

It is not surprising that I developed a love-hate relationship with Lark. After all, her birth took away my mother's attention. On the other hand, she offered companionship in a lonely house. The house was particularly lonely at that time because Sally and Sandy tried to spend as much time away as they could manage. Sally was in high school and often visited friends, while Sandy spent every possible hour at the local gas station.

Lark seemed to rely on me a great deal for guidance, and we received a lot of support from our maid, Marilyn. In fact, Marilyn and her sisters each provided us with mothering at different times. Lark was the most sensitive child; I could make her cry easily just by giving her a cross expression. An extremely talented artist, at an early age Lark had an uncanny ability to capture the sense of an animal on paper. In fact, my mother made such a fuss over Lark's paintings that I realized I would never equal her accomplishments and I gave up painting altogether.

I was slow to learn some of the basics. When I was in preschool, I discovered to my horror that most of the other kids knew something called the alphabet. When I got home, I was in tears as I ran into my mother's bedroom screaming, "I don't know the alphabet! Every other kid in my class knows it and I am too old to learn!" My mother immediately sat me down and taught me the alphabet.

First grade was a challenge. I was young for my class, but the school administrators said I tested well so I didn't need to go to kindergarten. Most of the other kids had been in kindergarten and I felt left out. I also did not like my first grade teacher. She seemed harsh and cold. Reading was a mystery to me. First she showed us how to read out loud; I could understand and carry that out. But when she said, "Now start reading with your eyes," I wondered what I had been reading with. The idea of silent reading stumped me for a long time, but my teacher was not very tolerant of my difficulty, and I was assigned to remedial reading. To make matters worse, my teacher was also our lunch monitor. I hated much of the food served in the dining hall—especially fishcakes. Secretly, I would slide them into a napkin on my lap and throw them into a corner of the stairwell when we left lunch. One day the lunch monitor saw I wasn't eating my fishcakes. She stood over me, "You must eat your lunch and I will stand here until you do." I forced the hideous tasting object into my mouth and started chewing. The next thing I knew I was spitting it out on my plate. She didn't require me to eat them after that, but the whole incident left me with bad associations.

Gilman School was full of Fisher history, and each year I became more aware of the Fisher legacy. My father's grandfather founded the school to create a safe country environment that would keep his grandchildren off the streets of Baltimore. The top prize of the school was the Fisher medallion. The dark, forbidding dining hall where I had my miserable encounter with the disgusting fishcakes was named the Fisher Dining Hall. Though I did not like being there and I never liked people telling me what to do, it never occurred to me to ask to change schools. I was a dutiful son and followed the family plan, which included Gilman School.

I was, however, delighted to learn how to write. And I really liked numbers; they were definite and you could get an answer. I can clearly recall writing the date in the upper right corner of my paper one day. I remember forming the 1949 and saying to myself, "I will always remember this day. Now I know what the date is and what it means." In a world that often seemed confusing, learning was a comfort. I was, however, disappointed in my handwriting and was quite jealous of a fellow student's skill. When I told my mother that a classmate had much better handwriting than I did, she said mine was fine and it was my very own. That made me feel better, but in fact my handwriting remained so poor that it "qualified" me to be a doctor.

I was driven to win and to be the best at sports and school. In retrospect, it's likely this was a way for me to gain the attention that I felt was lacking at home. I loved my third grade teacher, and she seemed to like me. She read a story of mine about a raccoon to the class as a good example; she said it had a lot of heart. One day I begged her to not get married until I was old enough to marry her, and she sweetly said, "That is very nice of you to want to marry me, and someday when you grow up, you will find a girl to marry." I don't know if she ever got married. In fourth grade, I recall a boy who got better grades than I did. Convinced there must have been something he was doing that led to his better grades, I watched his every move. I decided that the way he held his hands behind his back during prayer was the secret to his success. Each morning I would very carefully imitate the way he held his hands. I gave up after several weeks when I realized I still wasn't doing as well on my tests as my rival.

At the end of each school year, there was an event my mother dreaded watching —"field day." The climax of field day was a foot race. In my first three years, I was happy because I won, but in fourth grade, a boy named Freddie joined our class. He was really fast and he won every foot race after that. I was a poor loser and would cry after being defeated.

Another source of great frustration was my size. For a boy, being short can be traumatic and I was always short. I received nicknames that hurt, such as "shrimp boat." Class pictures were a painful reminder of my diminutive stature. I was one of the three shortest students and I was always placed in the first row. However, wrestling was a venue in which I could excel because we were matched for size. Wrestling also gave me a chance to release the aggressive feelings I had bottled up within, stemming from fear that bigger boys might beat me up. But my most frequent bully was my older brother Sandy, who didn't excel at athletics or school, and thus disappointed my father. Baseball in particular was very important to my father; he had played varsity baseball in college and hoped his son would as well. Sandy just couldn't throw a baseball and I could. I could be a real brat and would rub it in. So my father paid more attention to me. This left Sandy with a deep resentment, which he vented by hitting me so hard in the stomach that I lost my breath. When I was older I got even with my brother by wrestling him to his back.

When I was ten, I had a teacher who was also my wrestling coach. At that time, my favorite shirt was khaki with blue and gold corporal stripes sewn on the arm. Whenever I came up to his desk to ask him a question, he would drape an arm over me and put his hand down the back of my pants. This seemed odd, but I liked that he seemed affectionate. One weekend he had our class out to his family's farm. He showed us different insects in their stream, and afterwards gave us a delicious chocolate cake. Gradually, at school, he started taking me down to the basement of the fifth grade building. It was dark and was called "the dungeon." Those trips are still shrouded in darkness in my mind, but I do recall his asking me to drop my trousers. Some sort of forbidden exploration went on. He said I should not tell anyone about it. Luckily, the next year a friend of mine told his mother that this teacher was taking him down to "the dungeon" and exploring him. An investigation resulted in the teacher being placed in a psychiatric hospital and later leaving town. I must have been very ashamed, because it wasn't until many years later that I told my mother. Unfortunately, her response was, "It must not have been that serious or you would have told us." I had not had the heart to tell her. I shared very little with my parents. Years later I was able to connect the interruption in my emotional development and my psychoses to the trauma that took place when I was ten. My understanding of the impact of this trauma grew from therapy, the "Castle Dream" (which I describe later), and meditation.

At roughly the same time, my father developed Huntington's disease, which during the 1950s was considered such a dread illness that no one talked about it. His mother and grandmother had both had Huntington's. He was about fifty-two when it became clearly apparent. I was ten. He bravely went on practicing medicine until he was sixty-seven. At that point he could no longer drive, so his patients visited him at home. I do not recall his uttering a word about it. When he was seventy-five he was admitted to a nursing home. He had lost his ability to walk and needed assistance eating. When he was asked why he was admitted, he said he had "a mild case" of Huntington's disease. As I grew up I became aware that my siblings and I had a 50/50 chance of getting it.

As my father struggled silently with the symptoms of his disease, my mother and I grew very close again. She would engage in endless monologues, which started with the question, "What is the answer?" I wish I had asked her what the question was. Mostly, I recall her explaining her loss of faith in Christ. She had been raised Episcopalian, but clearly felt let down by that religion. She would say, "If Christ were divine, he would not have suffered. To me it is more important to think he was a man, because then he suffered. That means more to me than thinking that he was divine. So I want to become a Unitarian because they believe that Christ was no more divine than the rest of us. Therefore, whatever he accomplished we all can accomplish." I now think that her loss of faith in Christ was related to her loss of confidence in my father as he developed Huntington's.

Each Saturday I shared a special time with my father. He would take me to Johns Hopkins Hospital to accompany him on his rounds. Soon we were striding down the shiny marble floors with the sound of our footsteps echoing against the walls. At first I was puzzled. He would pull his chair up to the patient's bedside and would start a very general conversation about matters seemingly unrelated to the person's health. "Have you seen your family? How was your job going before you came here?" he would ask. During the course of the conversation he would gently lay his hand on the patient's and then feel their pulse. From my perspective as a child, the time he spent with each patient seemed endless, but the feelings of caring and concern were evident at every opportunity. After several hours of these rounds, we went across the street to Reed's Pharmacy where I invariably ordered a root beer float.

In her eighth year, my beautiful, clever, creative sister Lark began a lifetime of self-punishment. She refused to eat and became so anorexic she had to be hospitalized at Children's Hospital in Washington, D.C., for six months. Fortunately, she had the help of a child analyst. Gradually she started to eat again and my mother felt that the doctor was Christ-like. He asked how I was doing and my mother answered that I was perfectly normal. Prophetically he said, "Beware of the child who appears normal, as he may have problems later." None of us wanted to hear those words. Despite the likelihood that trauma was involved in Lark's anorexia, we all felt her problems were due to a chemical imbalance in her brain. I think our family adopted the belief that these problems were caused by a chemical imbalance because there was a strong tradition of doctors in our family and we did not want to look for trauma. She never seemed very happy after that period.

During these traumas, I had to become an adult child. I did not get a chance to fill in the missing elements of my development because I needed to be very serious and responsible. As a result, my voice was not my own. At school I used the voice that helped me get good grades. At home I used the voice that helped my family function. That's why when I look back, I liken myself to a mockingbird. In neither place, did I have an opportunity to develop my authentic Voice; I had no idea who I really was.

When I was sixteen and a high-school junior, I fell deeply in love for the first time. I fell for Marlene partly because she told me she found me attractive. She was fun to be with — we went to drive-in movies and steamed up the car windows. Though we had heated arguments about religion, I loved being with her. She was raised in a strict Catholic household and I tried to convince her that Unitarianism made much more sense. I just could not understand how she could believe in God. This troubled her. She also didn't like necking. She said her mother told her that led to sleeping together, which should be reserved for marriage. She was learning to drive, and I promised her she could drive my father's gray Vauxhall if she would French kiss. She conceded, but reluctantly. Then one day, in the spring, as we were driving back to her house I asked her to our junior prom.

"We can go as friends," she said.

I was shaken beyond belief. "Friends? What do you mean as friends?"

"We have gotten too close and I want to back off."

What a shot out of the blue that was. I thought I was going to black out. I felt desperate. It couldn't be true. She must be mistaken. That evening I just kept asking why she wanted to pull back. She told me we were too young to get so involved. I cried and cried. Later she told me she really worried about me because I cried so much. After that I said to myself, "Never let anyone get that close again."

She went to the junior prom with me, but we were frosty and hardly danced. After the dance, a bunch of us got together and we had many too many malt liquors. That introduced me to serious drinking; it felt good to numb myself to the emotional pain of the evening. Drinking was a welcome break from the rigid regimentation of my school and home life. That summer was also filled with coming-out parties. As a WASP (White Anglo Saxon Protestant) boy from a good Baltimore family, I received many invitations. The champagne flowed freely, and in retrospect, I am amazed I made it home some of those nights.

I turned to reason as a way to gain control of my feelings. I kept my feelings hidden, in good WASP tradition. I was a rational young man. My heart stopped talking to me. Who needed it anyway? It just seemed to cause pain.

When it came time to consider which college I would attend, there was no consideration. I had been carefully groomed to carry out the family tradition: I was to be a sixth-generation Princetonian. I had worn the T-shirt and been to the reunions. Also, Gilman was a feeder school for Princeton; ten of my fifty classmates went to Princeton. I was interviewed during October of senior year and was told I had been accepted for early admission, as long as I was not subject to any future disciplinary action. How ridiculous that sounded! I had always been such a well-behaved young man.

Then, a few weeks later, finding myself in jail, I recalled the admission officer's words. It all started as a prank on Halloween. We armed ourselves with dozens of rotten eggs. As night fell, we raced through upscale Roland Park in cars and on foot. One of the cars drove up on someone's lawn. I was racing down a sidewalk after a junior when I felt a tug on my arm, and a stern voice ordered me, "Drop that egg, sonny." I turned in horror to see the face of a police officer. He marched me and seven other students to a cruiser. We were taken to the police station because one of the boys had "armed himself" with homemade brass knuckles fashioned out of a locker handle. The boy said later, "I just wanted to be a big man." He stayed in jail overnight, while irate parents bailed out the rest of us. After serving the remainder of the school year on probation, our records were cleared and I was allowed to attend Princeton. We actually gained some notoriety from the escapade.

In retrospect, I was not ready to accept the daily responsibilities required to live away from home while attending college. My prep school was modeled after the English school tradition. It was long on discipline and short on self-expression and emotional connections. From seventh through twelfth grade, our almost entirely WASP student body at Gilman Country Day School for Boys was required to wear a jacket, tie, and slacks. As I was not a great shopper, I let my mother pick out my clothes. Starting in tenth grade, my shoes became my one form of personal expression. Instead of accepting the shoes my mother picked out, I started to buy what was popular among my friends, such as desert boots or suede saddle shoes. As for my hair, I had the barber cut it short and I parted it on the left side. In my early teens, I experimented with peroxide and Brylcreem, which was supposed to thrill the girls.

I am embarrassed to admit that we had a maid who took care of our laundry. She pressed, folded, and put away my clothes. So when I entered college, it is not surprising I was chaotic with my clothes. Freed of the rigid patterns of prep school, I wore whatever was handy. My roommate was aghast at my habit of stuffing my laundry into my bureau without folding it or worrying about wrinkles. He, in contrast, had each of his shirts pressed and folded. One day he said that I must be unhappy.

"Why, what makes you think that?" I asked defensively.

"I think the way you stuff your clothes into your bureau reflects your unhappiness," he replied. "Also, people have been asking me, 'What is wrong with your roommate, he seems so angry all the time?'"

Well, these comments made me angry and I made sure that the following year I found a roommate who shared an equal disregard for clothing.

Much of my later recovery of life involved learning to love and accept being loved. I feared getting close and subsequently losing a lover. I believed that if I didn't get involved, then losing someone would not be as painful. Getting close also felt dangerous. It meant that I would experience feelings more intensely and that was scary. I also feared that if I got close emotionally I would not be able to assert myself. I suspected I would need to carry out the wishes of my girlfriend, even if I disagreed with them. An illustration of these fears is my relationship with Joyce in college. I met her in the summer at a debutante party. She overheard me say that I was attending Princeton.

"That's not so great. I am going to Vassar," she interjected from across the table.

I admired her spunk and asked her to dance. We grew quite close that summer. We had our own song, "Sheila" by Tommy Roe. Gradually, though, the trait that attracted me to her — her outspoken manner — started to upset me. I learned that she could make decisions more quickly than I could because she was in closer touch with her emotions. I also learned that if she got angry she could express it and get over it. I, on the other hand, held in my anger. If I did let it out it was expressed as irritation about something relatively unrelated. For instance, during a speculative discussion about our possible future family, she began to plan where our children would attend church, namely her Protestant church. I, however, was raised Unitarian and did not agree. At first I went along with her plan, even though we had not even discussed marriage. However, inside I was seething. When I finally expressed my view, I was boiling mad and she was shocked. My anger lingered for several days.

I think I stayed in this relationship with Joyce in part due to her mother. Joyce's mother was wonderful and gave me little nuggets of insight into myself, which I had been missing at home. I accompanied her and her parents when they took her to college at the beginning of her freshman year. It was an emotional trip even though I did not realize why. I had controlled my own emotions about going to college the year before. On the trip home, I started singing a Ricky Nelson song, "Lonely Teenager." Joyce's mother made a comment about how sad the song was and wondered if I felt sad. I recall being surprised at her comment, since I was not aware of feeling sad or lonely. I did take note though and thought that the song did sound sad. I also was touched that she noticed. That experience was new to me.

Perhaps my biggest trauma with Joyce came during my sophomore year. A very important social event at Princeton was a "bicker," a type of rush that determined the eating club to which one would be admitted. Eating clubs are Princeton's version of fraternities, only snootier. The fifteen clubs were arranged in a social pecking order; at Princeton one's social standing was related to one's club membership. At the top of the social ladder was the Ivy Club, to which many of my relatives had belonged. To get invited into a high standing eating club you needed to have a cool room, cool roommates, and a cool personality. I failed in all three categories. On the first day of bicker, every club sends a review team to your room to assess you and your bicker mates' potential. As the week progresses, clubs that lose interest in you no longer send representatives. By the third day, we had very few reps visiting our room, and of those who still came, none were from the top tier clubs. I kept Joyce apprised of the situation and she began to panic. Not only is your prestige measured by your membership in an elite club, but so is your girlfriend's. At the end of the week I was only invited to a few of the bottom tier clubs: the bottom five. I was relatively passive and besides most of my friends had suffered the same outcome. However, Joyce was outraged and insisted that I petition for a better club. I was also pressured by an uncle to try for a better club. So, humiliating though it was, I circulated a petition for a better club. I got into the club I campaigned for, but a gray cloud hovered over the move. Several of my friends who went to the lesser club felt I had rejected them and dropped me. I had petitioned the better club to please my girlfriend and my family. This was one of many times that I felt that I had no Self of my own. I did not know who I was; I felt like a chameleon.

Joyce and I limped along for another year, but my heart was not in the relationship. I ended it badly in the middle of a vacation with her parents. We were on a porch, and it was a moonlit night. Joyce began talking about the wedding she thought we should have. I was feeling trapped. I did not want to be in the relationship, let alone married. Suddenly, without warning I stood up and said I could not continue with her. She was aghast, as I had given her no warning that this was coming. It certainly was a terrible time and place. Her father's reaction shocked me even more. In the past, he had always said how much he admired me and would brag to his friends about me. However, at this moment he said it was the right thing. He said we were never suited for each other anyway because I came from a family with many generations in the professional class and his family had only recently arrived in the lower management class. It was a long, silent, and painful three-hour car ride home. If I had only been able to know how I was feeling and able to discuss it, the break up would not have been an emotional tidal wave.

I had looked at love from both sides. In retrospect, I am reminded of the Joni Mitchell song, "Both Sides Now," and its refrain, "I really don't know love at all."

At roughly the same time, I was mapping out my career. At age eighteen, I told my father I wanted to find out more about mental illness. He suggested I visit Dr. Seymour Kety. I drove to Bethesda to meet him at the National Institute of Mental Health (NIMH). There were large imposing brick buildings, and Dr. Kety was head of the Laboratory of Clinical Science. His books, his position of authority, and his gray hair impressed me. It was 1962 and he was a high priest of science. Ten years earlier he had set up the labs of NIMH. I fell under his spell. I had thought of going to medical school, but he convinced me that the new frontier was neurochemistry.

"Neurochemistry is the field of the future. You shouldn't waste your time getting an MD. You should get a PhD in biochemistry. Then you could come back to NIMH and work in my lab," he told me.

Who could resist such an important man's recommendation? Not I. I would become a researcher and cure my sister's emotional distress. I would cure my father's Huntington's disease. I would be the family doctor. After all, someone from my generation had to be a doctor — there had always been a doctor. My father, my uncle, my grandfather, my great-grandfather, and so on back six generations were all doctors. It seemed I had little choice. The only decision I had to make was what type of doctor I would be. I would go to the laboratory and discover what was wrong with my family and cure them! I also felt a great relief to know what I would be doing for the next ten years.

Back at Princeton, I quickly decided to major in biochemistry. However, I was not a natural in the laboratory: my experiments often got mixed up and I was never very neat or organized in my work. With all the weight of tradition on my shoulders, I became convinced that I was a cog in the machinery of the world. We were all cogs and chemicals. My major goal was to discover the laws of the universe — especially the universe of the brain. In this way, I thought I could gain control of my life and fix it according to those prescribed laws. In retrospect, I experienced the world as being outside of me. The world was something to be discovered by instruments, not by experience. I was floating on the surface of life — well-versed and well-spoken but never getting emotionally close to anyone. My sister Lark could see I was in that artificial state.

She drew me aside one day in 1963 and said, "You've got to listen to this song by Bob Dylan. He is singing about you."

He was singing the "Ballad of a Thin Man." As he scratched out the words with his raspy voice, I felt a shudder of life trying to stir inside of me. I especially felt he was speaking to me when he said, "Something is happening and you don't know what it is, do you, Mr. Jones?"

On November 22, 1963, I shared a trauma with the rest of the nation. Nearly everyone who was alive in 1963 remembers where they were on that day. I was leaving a Religious Ideas in Literature class when I heard students shout reports that President Kennedy had been shot. It didn't seem possible, but it was. How could our young, inspiring President be dead? Soon I was nauseous and ready to vomit. I spent the next day in the infirmary paralyzed with disbelief. A few days later I went to my grandmother's home for Thanksgiving with Lark and Uncle Moyne. My uncle was still in mourning clothes from the funeral. He had been a roommate of Kennedy's in high school and during freshman year at Princeton; they had been best friends.

During the following year, my senior research advisor, Dr. Arthur Pardee, was constantly warning me to be more careful. Whenever he walked into my lab he would start moving glassware away from the edge of the lab bench and say, "Most lab accidents happen because glassware is too close to the edge of the bench." He terrified me, but my motivation to cure my family carried me through the lab work. A roommate in college had tried to warn me by saying, "You don't seem like the type of person to go into research. You seem too interested in people." To which I replied, "If you really want to do something badly enough you can do it." I knew he was right but I felt what I *wanted* to do was not as important as doing what important people told me I *should* do. I was convinced that by doing research I would discover the biochemical basis of my family's unhappiness. I stayed at Princeton that summer to complete the research I had started as an undergraduate and managed to get publishable research out of my work. I was accepted at the University of California at Berkeley and the University of Wisconsin. I decided on Wisconsin, because Berkeley seemed too radical.

At the end of the summer, I spent several days with my mother, father, and Lark at Rehoboth Beach, Delaware, where we had a good time. So I was really puzzled by how dramatically Lark and my mother cried when I was ready to leave. My father was stoic as always. It never occurred to me that this would be our last family vacation together. But they were keenly aware that it was. Later, I found out that they felt they were truly losing me.

I was heading to the distant Midwest. As I drove away, I was still wondering about their tears. I was so self-contained that it never occurred to me until many years later how attached they were to me. I first drove to Cold Spring Harbor, Long Island, where I gave a scientific talk on my work with Dr. Pardee. I was awed by the audience, which included James D. Watson, who co-discovered the structure of DNA with Francis Crick. Then I crawled into my VW Beetle, which contained all my earthly possessions, and drove twenty-four hours straight to Madison, Wisconsin. A new education awaited me there: a political education.

Like many kids of my generation, I hit the late '60s like a wall. We had lived the "Leave it to Beaver" life of the '50s. We were regimented and industrialized. Television provided a model of the perfect family, with father appearing to know best (though mother quietly was the power behind the throne). We were taught that for every problem there was a technical solution. We believed DuPont's slogan "Better Living through Chemistry," and in achieving the American Dream of every family in its own house behind its own picket fence. The baby boomers were born into the middle of this dream...or nightmare. I was born during World War II, so I had some memory of life before the saturation of television. Our family did not get our first television set until 1953. During the peak of my hippie days, when I was twenty-seven, I recall a young woman of nineteen saying she envied my generation; she said that at least we had had an opportunity to see what life had been like before it was turned upside down by the student revolts of the '60s. She had a point. I am older than the baby boomers and yet I identify with them; I was twenty-five when I first took mescaline.

The stereotyped world of my parents and my East Coast WASP existence began to slip away in 1965 as I drove my VW to Madison. Inside the mechanical self that I had become, a seedling of new consciousness was taking root in that Midwestern soil. A new me, closer to my genuine Self, started to push up through the cracks of my former self.

Madison was already hopping with political activity when I arrived. I found a cooperative restaurant, the Green Lantern, to be a far cry from the eating clubs of Princeton. There were no waiters and the members did all the work except the cooking. One hundred and twenty members paid $7.50 a week for lunch and dinner, six days a week. After dinner, radical student leaders would lecture on the evils of American imperialism and the need to end the Vietnam War. They would tell us where to assemble for the next demonstration. I resisted their analysis at first. I was still a believer in our government. But they were forming larger cracks in my certainty.

One day, a friend, Loren, said, "Surely you don't believe the Warren Commission Report? You know it was a cover up."

I was markedly disturbed by this allegation. How could he be right? But he was passionate and well-informed. For me, losing President Kennedy had been like losing a member of the family. Loren went on, "I worked with attorney Mark Lane and we found that the Warren Report was a cover up. The evidence shows that there was a conspiracy, and that it was not just the act of a lone gunman." He cited Mark Lane's book *Rush to Judgment*. I listened, I talked, I read,

I thought, and I decided he was right. Then I asked myself, "If the government had lied about the Kennedy assassination, what else had they lied about?" Loren had an answer to that question. He asked me, "Why do you think we are at war in Vietnam?" I gave the standard government response, "We are in Vietnam to fight Communism. If Vietnam falls then all the countries in Southeast Asia will become Communist." He shook his head, "No, we are in Vietnam to protect our economic interests. Our corporations need their raw materials." As I listened, I could hear the concrete certainty of my preppy self cracking up. I went from blind faith to blind doubt. I wondered who or what could I trust.

Another warning that I needed to change came when an acquaintance drew me aside and told me she was concerned about the way I related to people. She said I was congenial on the surface but she and others noticed that I never allowed people to get emotionally close. Her words rang a bell and were painful because I knew deep down she was right. She had seen how carefully I defended myself. This neatly constructed way of being — or not being — had propelled me through my first twenty-two years in an efficient, barely emotional fashion.

During the winter of my first year in graduate school, I met Sarah, who seemed to express some of the emotions I lacked. We grew close, especially when I sided with her, against her father, in opposition to the war in Vietnam. Sarah was uncomfortable with my scientific approach to life. I believe that loneliness and the feeling that I should be involved with someone prompted me to live with her. Then, shortly after turning twenty-three, I married her because I had the old-fashioned belief that people should get married if they sleep together. I also remember thinking that I was the right age to get married. I was still trying to run my life like a program or a school assignment. I would ask authorities what was the right thing to do, and then carry out their plan regardless of how I felt about it. I was programmed to be a biochemist and to get married. Sarah didn't really want to get married, but I talked her into it. On our wedding day, my brother asked me if I had any reservations. "None at all," I said very confidently, as if I were about to take another exam.

In actuality, I was feeling very little in those days: I was too frightened of feelings to feel. It didn't work. In fact, to my wife's dismay I awoke one night screaming, "All I want are the facts — the hard cold facts." My unemotional approach left her feeling cold and unconnected to me. We did not have an intimate relationship and I spent more and more time in the lab. When I was home I heard criticism. She asked me to remember to close the shower curtain after a shower or to avoid leaving crumbs on the table. I would complain that she cooked the same dishes every night.

My three years in Madison were marked by struggle between my old self and new Self. My old self went on dutifully measuring chemicals, trying to discover the mysteries of cell growth under the guidance of Dr. Gerald Mueller. I was trying to develop the skills and knowledge to cure my father's Huntington's and my sister's anorexia. My new Self was questioning the relevance of such a career in a world that appeared to be turning upside down.

I was determined to get out of Dr. Mueller's lab in three years. I saw too many graduate students who were languishing there for seven or eight years. I first had to get into the Public Health Service because I wanted to avoid being sent to Vietnam, and working at NIMH could be my duty station. So I wrote Dr. Kety at NIMH. In response, I received a letter from Dr. Jack Durell. He informed me that Dr. Kety had left NIMH but that I could come and work with him. So back to NIMH I returned, six years after Dr. Kety had given me my instructions.

Dr. Durell had a smoother demeanor than I was accustomed to. He was dressed in a dapper suit and he didn't look or sound like a researcher. He was a psychiatrist and told me, "You would do well to work with me. It would further your career because I am respected in the field. I am overseeing research, but I am also opening psychiatric hospitals." I questioned this and decided I needed to find a real researcher. So I went to the NIMH directory and found Dr. Seymour Kaufman. I recalled that he had made an important contribution to the biochemistry of amino acid synthesis. He had discovered a vital cofactor, which was named a pterin. I had read of this compound but had never heard it pronounced. I went to visit his lab and was very impressed by his appearance. Although he was a senior scientist, he still wore a white lab coat — and it was even dirty. It seemed clear that he still worked in a lab. I was such a good mockingbird, that I knew he would want to hear that I was impressed by his work. So I told him what a great discovery he had made in finding that pterins were required for tyrosine bio-synthesis. When I pronounced pterins, I did so with an audible letter P.

He corrected me, "You mean pterins," pronouncing the word with a silent P.

"Yes, that was what I meant."

I told him that I had also seen Dr. Durell, but I failed to tell him how he disappointed me.

"Yes, I know Jack, he is friend of mine. He tells me to watch TV whenever I get depressed."

I told him of my educational background.

"Well you got off to a good start going to Princeton, but I am not sure about Wisconsin."

Though he seemed a little too status conscious, I asked if I could work in his lab and he agreed.

Back I went to back Madison, to defend my thesis.

Two

Finding my Unique Voice

The day in September 1968 when I completed my PhD defense should have been one of the happiest days of my life. I was twenty-four and had obtained a PhD in biochemistry. I clearly remember fairly skipping out of the office where five senior scientists declared I had done a good job on my research and had passed the requirements. I ran into the lab and everyone cheered. I called my wife, who had left for Washington, D.C., three weeks earlier to find us an apartment.

"Guess what, Sarah! I just passed my thesis defense."

After a silence, all she said in a voice as cold as stone was, "That's great." My heart sank.

I knew something was very wrong. During the next day, I tried to keep myself busy with goodbyes and packing, distracting myself from the icy tone in Sarah's voice. After landing at National Airport, I rushed to embrace Sarah, thinking everything would be all right. But her stiff, impersonal, physical reaction told me otherwise.

"We have to talk," were her fateful words.

That night at dinner she dropped the bomb. Our marriage was over and she wanted to leave. I felt my world crumble. I asked her to explain the reason she wanted to leave me. She cited my cold scientific approach to life. In retrospect, who could blame her? Yet at the time I blamed her mightily.

When Sarah left, my old self cracked apart. I was twenty-four, PhD in hand, and starting a dream job at NIMH. Yet I was face down on the floor under the shadow of Poe's raven, quoting, "nevermore." "The Raven" was well-illustrated by the painting on a tray by my sister, Lark.

And the raven, never flitting, still is sitting, still is sitting
On the pallid bust of Pallas just above my chamber door;
And his eyes have all the seeming of a demon's that is dreaming.
And the lamplight o'er him streaming throws his shadow on the floor;
And my soul from out that shadow that lies floating on the floor
Shall be lifted — nevermore!

Another work by Poe, the story "The Descent into the Maelstrom," captures my feelings of that time. In it, a fisherman recounts a fantastic story about his survival after being sucked down into a giant whirlpool, a maelstrom. In my early years, I had a fear of being trapped in a tunnel and later became preoccupied with spirals. I tried to focus on the outward turnings of spirals, but a friend convinced me they were an indication of death. The combination of a tunnel and an inward turning spiral started to feel like a whirlpool sucking me down. During these tumultuous years, I felt as if I was being sucked down into a maelstrom of despair and hopelessness. The first spins downward were liberating. Indeed, I may have had to go through them to break the grip that duty had upon my soul. In the Poe story, the descent into the maelstrom may have represented the fisherman's confrontation with his fear of death. Notably he sees a rainbow at the bottom of the maelstrom, which he calls the bridge between time and eternity. This theme of rainbows and arches will appear later in my life.

A few days after Sarah moved out, I wrote the following:

Much precious time has passed since I addressed myself to my nature. I used to worry much about my isolation from the world of senses and action. Sex was a big hang- up. I used to ponder the emotion/reason question. I can clearly remember one of my first reflections after reading Plato in June 1962 during which I opted for reason over emotion in a very reasoned manner. I pointed out that my mother had similarly opted. The wheel turns and six years later I say I was being defensive and feared to give reign [sic] to my emotions, perhaps due to a dread of what I really was. I used to write as if I was a great essayist and not myself, but full of affectation. Today the search for me begins. Who am I? Where have I been all these years of apparent success? I feel much of myself is hidden.

I will briefly review the recent events that brought me to my present state. I cherish these events because they have gouged down to my humanity sufficiently to get this visceral response.

I then wrote about how badly my relationship with my wife had deteriorated that summer, followed by this reflection:

Perhaps she was upset with my inability to get mad? Perhaps more deeply at getting married, period. She would tell me the magic had gone and she didn't really love me anymore. She only loved me occasionally. To make matters worse, I still loved her. I suggested a marriage counselor and she just laughed. So a long summer dragged on. Neither of us wished to talk heart-to-heart because it only meant tears.

Monday came and the journey home to tell of my misfortune. Can any man have suffered such a misfortune? My mother was not very sympathetic. I was furious, yet I did not express the anger. Disgustingly I reveled in the role and saw nothing wrong with it as a reflection. I hardly ever expressed anger or dissatisfaction with my mother throughout my childhood.

This was the first writing I had done about my inner dialogue for more than a year.

Two weeks before Sarah left, I again entreated her to go to couples therapy.

She laughed, "What's the use? I don't want to be married."

She agreed to go to one session with a very skilled social worker. At the end of the session the social worker said that I should go into psychoanalysis.

"You have great potential that you are not able to fulfill because of your emotional distress. You are like the main character in Dostoevsky's novel, *The Idiot*. Therapy will help you unlock that potential."

I felt optimistic. The therapist recommended that Sarah continue to see her individually. Sarah moved out the next week; she was adamant. Suddenly I felt unbearably lonely in our two-bedroom apartment near DuPont Circle.

Shortly after Sarah left, I wrote the following letter to my mother, which I never sent. I think I felt the letter was too honest to send and yet I needed to understand more deeply what I was feeling about my mother:

> *Dear Mother,*
>
> *Did we ever really communicate during the important years? I think not. Not for my part at least. Not the important inner feelings, only the amenities and superficialities. I don't mean to hurt you. You have made the best of a bad deal. No better can be done. This is more for my benefit, for I am at last realizing the abyss of lost self all around and especially behind me. Were we really frank with each other? No. All that talk about my being perfect was and still is extremely damaging to the real fallible me.*
>
> *Remember the story Gram used to tell about perfection. When Cousin John was about five, Gram told him that his father was perfect.*
>
> *Little John disagreed, and said, "Granmommy, nobody is perfect."*
>
> *Gram replied, "Your father is perfect."*
>
> *John stuck to his view, "If you had to live with him, Granmommy, you wouldn't think he was perfect."*
>
> *Well I felt the same way about myself. Nobody is perfect. Indeed it is our imperfections that make us human. And I have plenty enough*

to make me very human. Putting me in the perfect role was probably a very real need you had, considering how the other kids were behaving. I sensed this need and was more than obliging. I have come to believe it myself and have attempted the impossible, to actually be "The Golden Boy." The implications of such an attempt have been devastating. I have never gotten on well with other people in a close manner.

Superficially I am fine, but when it comes to heart-to-heart interactions I fail. Why? I think a great deal because I have this sense of superiority, which comes across as conceit and egotism. Who could like such a person who has an obvious lack of warmth, humility, etc. and is always more intent upon humbling and showing up another person than upon building them up, praising, or especially having any regard for them as another human being? Yes, that is the way I view my fellow man. Ironic you say, you thought I got along marvelously with others just as I did (did I?) with you. You have indoctrinated Lark with the same view. Poor thing, she always thought I was the most popular in my class. Completely false: I was an outcast; an oddball and I seemed to revel in it. My solution to this problem with other people was to decide that I really didn't need them; that I was the independent sort and could do without my fellow man. And so I led a very lonely childhood in the name of independence and self-reliance; what terribly false defense mechanisms those were for me. My, how dexterous I was at erecting defense mechanisms.

Another one was my lack of perception. I think I am basically a very perceptive person, and yet for years people have told me how little I perceive. Generally I would write them off as wrong, but were they? In some ways they were right. For I think I anesthetized my perceptions so as to avoid the inevitable pain, which would have ensued from facing what I really was, especially in relationships with other people. My motive for such a conscious dulling of perception was strong. At stake was the view of myself derived from you. Namely that I was perfect.

Full exercise of my perception would have revealed that I was far from perfect. But such a contradiction would have caused great anxiety. Thus, let us not look carefully at what other people say or think, do not believe anyone but yourself, and don't be truthful with yourself. This way I nicely isolated myself from the hard realities. Remarkably, my confrontations with cold reality were quite infrequent. Naturally when they *came I was bitterly shocked and temporarily shaken. One such incident was being rejected by Marlene in my junior year. Oh, how bitterly I wept when she said I was not her knight in shining armor. Apparently she was worried about my future after that night. Now I can understand her concern. I had been going out with her for only three months, weekends and had not received great encouragement. Yet there I was weeping for hours over her saying she did not want to be with me. The other incident was at a debutante party at the Elkridge Club. I was sitting with my back to Johnny Stockbridge and could hear him saying to someone, "That Fisher is really different (or odd?)." I was shocked, though I had spent my life cultivating such an image.*

Two other shocking realities I could not avoid during my youth were my physical size and the competition of others. The impact that my small size had upon me is not to be underestimated. I was considerably shorter than the average height for my age. No amount of perceptual dulling or self-deception could hide that fact. It was a real everyday reality that could not disappear with a night's sleep. I recall feeling very badly about being shorter and having everyone look down on me. It is very difficult to feel superior to people who are looking down at you. And then there is competition — I have always been very competitive. Why? Because this was another means of testing the image of perfection and superiority, which had been woven for me by you. I had to win merely to be consistent with the image, and any loss — be it at field day, pounce [family card game], or grades — came as a great blow. Indeed one that was worthy of tears. How could someone who approached games with such a spirit be a good sport? Impossible.

Then there is the matter of emotions. If you are going to be really truthful with someone you really care about, then you have to let down your mask and barriers and be yourself. Well, I am only willing to let down so much and then I stop. I can't allow them to get to know me anymore than I know myself and that is quite limited. And then the games must begin: the games of not being myself. Not responding in an emotional manner from fear of what might come out. Afraid to get mad for fear of losing love, though the inability to express anger actually loses love. The expression of love itself loses spontaneity. Instead of intensive, bursts of love, I express a steady deadening affection, which is soon exposed as a dependency, a clinging on merely for the sake of having someone around.

It is complex how people interact in an intimate relationship where so much depends on one expressing one's feelings, and when you can't do that to yourself, obviously it is impossible to do it for another. So rather than not talk, I intellectualize, talking the way I think things ought to be, rather than feeling the way things are with me here and now. I guess again a lot of this hang up is due to the old perfection image of Dan. If Dan is indeed "The Golden Boy," then he can only do and feel golden things. So if he feels things that are not golden, such as hate or depression, there is a great conflict between what I am (fallible in my feelings and in my inability to hear criticism) and what I felt I should be, Why? Because someone who is perfect can do no wrong and therefore the criticism must be wrong, as well as what you would have me be, which is perfect in my feelings and impulses. This brings me to the question of good and evil. In both my deep relationships, with Joyce and Sarah, I was constantly told I was a good person. Well maybe I am, but I am not sure. I do good things and act in a good manner in accord with my necessary image, but do I feel these good deeds and good words? I think not. They, as with my emotions, are empty mouthings. Whether I am good or evil should be irrelevant. I should be me first of all, and do away with these superficial labels of transient cultural values.

So from above it should become apparent that I am not perfect, far from it. And as close as I attempt to be perfect, I remain that same distance from being me. I entreat you to look carefully and thoroughly inside yourself for the reasons why I was (and am) pictured as perfect, rather than human. And again I emphasize that they are mutually exclusive. Ironic that you should reject the divinity of Christ on the grounds that it spoils his humanity, and yet not worry about spoiling, destroying my humanity, in order to heap divinity upon me. It has perhaps been therapeutic for you, but unhealthy for me.

As to the matter of responsibility, I feel that I am heaping too much of it upon you and not accepting enough myself. I had at all times the choice to act otherwise, though in retrospect the course is not clear or easy. I should have pointed out long ago the depth of my weaknesses and the damage that overlooking them was doing. I should not have allowed myself to live in such self-deception. I should have confronted myself with the fact that I was behaving very abnormally indeed. Also, above all I should have realized long ago that I need and cherish others. (As I now believe is a human need). Perhaps for a genius (which I am not) or the artist (which I am not) their work can be their life. But since I will not achieve such Leviathanic heights, and am interested in such mundane things as marriage and a child, I should be realistic about the importance of people in this!

A week later I wrote:

Now a month and several psychiatrists later I sit alone in my apartment on this Sunday morning. Lost in an uncharted sea, a position I have assiduously avoided for my whole life. Sarah lives a block away. For us the future is dim. I want only to forget her and be done with it. Divorce after a respectable time and start anew. However, that is not the rational, advisable way. We are still very tied up with each other by our own vocal and tearful admissions of Thursday night. So we must remain each in our own uncharted sea and trust only in time; she also in her marriage counselor and friends, and me in my psychiatrist and friends. For me today is momentous in as much as I must decide whether or not to begin psychoanalysis. So I ask myself, am I so screwed up that I need it?

I entered psychoanalysis at Chestnut Lodge with Dr. James Bullard, the son of the founder of the Lodge. (This was the place that helped Joanne Greenberg heal, as described in her book *I Never Promised You a Rose Garden*, written under the pseudonym Hannah Green.) Five days a week I drove out to Rockville, Maryland, for an eight o'clock appointment. Five days a week I lay transfixed on the couch, staring at Dr. Bullard's acoustic tile ceiling, dutifully obeying instructions to say whatever came to my mind. After two months of spewing out all manner of history, I turned to my analyst and asked him to provide the insight, the mental mechanism to fix the broken machinery of my mind. I told him I viewed analysis as a car repair shop. In my view, I came in and told him everything I felt was wrong, then he, the psychic mechanic, would apply his psychic wrench with an insight, which would solve my problems. Thankfully, he refused and my old self crumbled further.

"What is this need you have to have me fix you?"

He was clearly putting the responsibility back in my hands.

Being in therapy made me want to find out more about my parents. They had kept so much secret, especially my father. I remember one night Lark and I cornered our father. We asked him what he had been thinking all the years we were growing up.

"I was just glad to be able to be around the family," he said.

I was horrified. "It sounds to me that you felt like a guest in our house," I exclaimed.

"Yes, I felt like a guest," he agreed.

Then we asked him what he had thought of the recent Thanksgiving dinner.

"Well there were some strong men there," he shared.

"What do you mean, there were strong men there?" I said with dismay.

"There was LeMoyne, Chuck, and Sandy; they are real men," he solemnly declared.

"But you didn't mention me," I answered, incredulously.

"Well, I am not sure about you," he ended the discussion with that statement.

Lark and I were stunned. This was one of the few windows into our father's thoughts, and the revelations were worrisome. His issues about manhood and not feeling that he belonged in the family had shown up before. This however, was the first time we heard him say so.

I am now dismayed that the issue of my family's legacy of Huntington's disease did not come up more often in my therapy. The topic was rarely raised at home, but I felt as if I had the sword of Damocles hanging above my head. Having a 50/50 risk of inheriting Huntington's has made me run through my life like the White Rabbit in *Alice in Wonderland*. My father's mother had the disorder, which manifests itself as a gradual degeneration of the nervous system. By the time I saw her, she was confined to her bed in a nursing home, unable to speak or feed herself. It was a terrible, undignified sight that I witnessed every

Sunday until she died in 1955. I was eleven at the time of her death. When she died it was already clear that my father was getting it too. Fortunately, in our family the onset comes later than in most families. But as children we were all aware of the threat hovering over us like a premature death sentence.

Gradually my strong, disciplined father succumbed like his mother. Slowly over time, there was less and less he could do. Because we rarely spoke of his decline, it grew to be an even greater worry. I would, like the rest of the family, put on a brave face to the world. When friends of my parents inquired about my father, I would always say he was fine. They, in turn, would politely not pry.

One day, we were at a local cafeteria. My father was the last in line. The cashier called me back and asked me to carry my father's tray, as she was concerned he could not manage. At first he resisted, but to avoid a scene he allowed me to carry his tray to the table. We ate in silence and never returned to the cafeteria again. In his early sixties, he was told he should stop driving. Then walking became difficult and he had to give up going to the office to see his patients. They adored him so much, however, that they insisted on continuing to see him at our house. His last five years in a nursing home were similar to what his own mother had endured. He faced the ordeal with incredible grace and dignity.

Despite my wife's leaving, or perhaps because of it, I continued to focus on the possibility that I could bring happiness to the world through my work in the laboratory. I did not realize that it was my own unhappiness I needed to deal with first. I did not understand that feelings can not be found in a test tube. They exist *in vivo* (in life) not *in vitro* (in glass). Unfortunately, I became trapped in my own construct of reality. After being a fairly easy-going kid, I emerged as a very serious adult whose main mission was to find the chemical responsible for schizophrenia, and a way to correct the chemical imbalance I believed caused it.

My boss at NIMH, Seymour, was the consummate chemist. He was convinced that one should be able to write a formula for every aspect of life. His favorite word was "mechanism." I followed his lead and together we explored the deepest secrets of the enzymes that regulate the production of the neurotransmitters dopamine, serotonin, and norepinephrine: phenylalanine hydroxylase, tyrosine hydroxylase, and tryptophan hydroxylase. They were the Holy Grail of neurochemistry. I was a very good biochemist and came up with a lot of formulae. In fact, after five years of work I had found at least forty different variables, such as heat, oxygen, salt, iron, etc., that profoundly affect the activity of those enzymes and which regulate the brain's chemical balance.

Yet, the more deeply I delved into the chemistry of these neurotransmitters, the more I started to doubt my own self. I started to feel that these reactions had a life of their own. I started to feel that I was a biochemical machine. This troubled me: where was I in all this chemistry? I was losing faith in the two Seymours' biochemical explanation for life. All these chemicals were dumb: they needed a person with thoughts and feelings to tell them which way to go. These thoughts made it harder and harder for me to feel good about going to the lab. But it was my chosen career; I only had to hold out for another twenty-six years and I could retire at age fifty-one. However, it didn't seem right to be counting my years to retirement when I was only twenty-five.

Thus, I began to lead a double life. By day, I pretended to remain interested in science and research at NIMH, but at night, I explored altered states of consciousness and began to open my artistic Self. My life became a struggle between the two selves residing inside me. The old self dutifully trudged to the neurochemistry lab each day, sorting out the mechanisms of neurotransmitters with a hope of discovering the biochemical basis of schizophrenia and Huntington's disease. Meanwhile, I was giving birth to a new me inside. That Self was the emotional, artistic, political Self. That was the Self that wanted to taste the world and respond and be a part of the flow of humanity.

My old self tightened its grip. "Don't let go of me, I am all you know," it said. But I knew my old ways of thinking and not being had not worked. I was furious at my mechanical, linear past. I needed to discover a new way of being. No half measures! I assaulted my citadel of linear thinking from every angle. Through modern dance, political theatre, communal living, and hallucinogens, I worked to crack wide open that old self.

Gradually, I started building a new life. I took an art course at the Corcoran Museum, with an instructor who was a Chilean Marxist. My first assignment was to create shapes that could be displayed on a board. I poured plaster into thirty hollow Styrofoam cubes. When I proudly displayed my monotonous series of thirty identical pyramids glued to a board, the instructor said I did art like an industrialist. I knew he was right and realized I must undo my mechanized side to create art and to create a new life.

I turned to political protest after a life of complacently accepting the status quo. I turned to people and found it harder and harder to believe in my work at the laboratory. I explored other realities through smoking marijuana. I went through a number of short-term relationships, feeling I had to prove myself as a man. Then I settled down for about nine months with Nancy. We went on an adventurous trip to Colombia during which we visited my brother. We also traveled up the Amazon for five days in a thirty-foot dugout powered by a tiny engine. I started to experience sides of myself I had never imagined were there.

I would arrive at the lab doubtful that we could ever discover deeper truths of existence in a glass test tube. I had realized that we are all much more than a collection of chemicals, and I lost faith in the work I had spent seven years of study to undertake. My PhD seemed meaningless. I tried to continue with the scientific method of generating a hypothesis, carrying out the experiment, and then analyzing the results to see if the evidence supported or destroyed my hypothesis.

Unfortunately I was using myself as the experimental subject, with my memories of my past self as a control. I would struggle for the next six years with conflicting views of my Self and the world. **Was I — and every other human — just a robot consisting of biochemical reactions and mechanical movements? Or were we uniquely human, each of us with our own hopes, dreams, and loves that could not be reduced to chemistry?** If the latter was the truth, what should I do now?

On a fateful fall day in 1969, I gave a major speech at the Fourth Annual Leukocyte Culture Conference at Dartmouth College. I swiftly explained the mechanisms of cell growth, which I had elucidated in my PhD work. I systematically delivered what was to be my last hard-science speech: "The Mechanism of Cell Growth Is Initiated by the Turnover of Phosphatidylinositol in the Cell Membrane." Though I had lost faith in the importance of my work, I described the step-by-step unfolding of chemical changes, which I had discovered as early precursors of cell growth. (See page x, "My transformation from isolated scientist to humanitarian.")

As I walked down from the podium, a bearded graduate student stopped me, "Man, that was a cool speech. Were you stoned?"

"No, I was straight," I replied.

"Come with us, we are trying out a new drug."

In the cool, dappled New Hampshire afternoon, we took a small purple pill (mescaline, they said) that launched me down a road of no return. I was like Alice tumbling down the rabbit hole, for that trip opened up so much inside me that I realized I had to change.

At one moment I was walking up a road and suddenly I realized that my wife was walking up the same road; we were just humans struggling to make meaning out of the mystery of life. I was able to forgive her at that moment, and I started to feel free from the hatred that had consumed me during the year since she left. At another moment, I was standing on a rock in the middle of a creek when it suddenly occurred to me that everyone on the earth at that moment was connected to everyone else. On reflection, this insight also tells me how disconnected I had been feeling prior to this experience. Unfortunately, that trip also opened long-locked doors, and the dazzling light that poured in blinded me.

Several weeks later, the same graduate student contacted me, wanting to know if I would join him to trip on mescaline again. Both of us would bring our girlfriends along this time. Away in rural New York, the trip was thrilling and insightful. It seemed that for the first time since childhood I was able to feel genuine emotions. I sensed the very dimensions of my Self were expanding. I had eidetic imagery, where you can hold a visual image far longer than usual. Nancy and I watched fireflies over a field. Gradually I could discern a pattern of communication among the fireflies. They initiated a set of flashes at one end of the field and then they moved across the field in a steady fashion, like waves on the ocean. Once they reached the far side they reflected back again. All my senses were alive, much as I remembered when I was a child. Gradually the effects wore off, and we returned to the mundane life and consciousness of the everyday world. I played a song by The Moody Blues from their album, *A Question of Balance*. I was particularly moved by the idea it communicated of achieving balance through Self-understanding. As the lyrics describe, "I opened my eyes and I realized the way it had always been." But my eyes only remained open a short while, and once the mescaline wore off I found myself back in a relationship that felt deadening, back at NIMH in a lab where I felt deadened, and back in analysis, which was also very deadening.

Several weeks after the trip to rural New York and seeking a return to that dreamy state of connection, I took another pill. I thought it was mescaline though it looked different. I realize now it was probably STP ("Serenity Tranquility Peace"), a psychedelic that stays in one's system for three to four days, in contrast to mescaline, which is metabolized in eight to ten hours. So my girlfriend and I each took that fateful pill in the mountains of the Shenandoah Forest. It was a golden afternoon, but that trip did not start well. I felt nauseous and disoriented. Soon I became mistrustful. We got lost in the forest and barely found our way back. As we passed a dump and saw two large bears, I felt sheer fright. I was sure they were somehow accusing me of all the intrusions into their space. I sensed that I had to make a promise to them that I would protect them before they let me pass. Later, I couldn't sleep. I had bizarre images of bears attacking, of having been poisoned, and of not being able to trust my girlfriend. I remember she said to me at one point, "Whoever your mother was, she must have been a fighter." I was left wondering, "Who was my mother? Who am I?"

The next morning I managed to drive us back to Washington in my trusty Volvo. But my paranoia heightened steadily during the day. It seemed there were police everywhere and I was convinced they were after me. I felt I had to get rid of everything, including my girlfriend. She worked in the Sleep Lab at NIMH, and I became convinced that her lab was experimenting on me. When we got back to the city I told her we were through. This was shocking and frightening to her and I am sure I hurt her. Maybe in some way I felt I had to get even with Sarah for having left me.

The instant I told her we were through she flashed a smile and said, "Now you have all the power." To me that meant she had felt she had the power before — which is what I had suspected.

I returned home to my shared house on S Street. My room was a mess and all I could think was that I should give everything away. This was a recurrent theme when I wanted to break up with a lover; I felt I had to get rid of all my possessions at the same time. I viewed the world in terms of everything or nothing. I withdrew into our house, trying to make sense of the chaos spinning in my head. I joined my housemate Leon and his therapy group for dinner. But the food was very spicy and I felt nauseous. I went to bed and tried to sleep. I could feel my heart pounding, and a song by the Eagles was ringing in my ears, "Don't let the sound of your own wheels drive you crazy."

Deeper and deeper I traveled until I was no longer speaking, no longer even moving. I felt poisoned, paralyzed, and unable to move. I was sure television cameras were surrounding the house. I thought the cameras were there to watch me because of crimes that I had committed. I thought and thought. I tried to think what I had done wrong, what had been my mistake. I suspected that I was connected with President Kennedy's assassination. I was worried that my uncle was angry with me because I no longer believed in this country — that he was angry that I had been demonstrating against the war in Vietnam. That was the reason I had been poisoned. I suspected my mother was an accomplice. I was trying to find out what my identity was. I imagined that my father had been tortured at Johns Hopkins because he had been disobedient. I imagined that they had put a radio receiver into his back so they could direct him. I wanted to call my parents but I suspected I could not trust them. I wanted to tell Leon, but could not trust him. I was wary that he had been involved in the poisoning. I felt my muscles were paralyzed. The world and everyone in it appeared to have died. I did not yet realize that I felt dead inside. I struggled to keep two sides of my psyche separated, as I had done most of my life. But I also badly wanted to be whole, to be united, and connected. Each side of me seemed like a sun, a bright, burning ball of fire. One ball of fire seemed to be in my head and the other in my spine. One part of me felt it was vital that the two suns come together while the other side was saying no, that would be a disaster. Finally, exhausted, I could no longer hold them apart and there was a blinding flash of light. I was convinced I had died and then I passed out.

When I woke up the next morning I was convinced I had been through a catastrophe. I awoke in deep confusion about who I was. (My experience was very close to John Weir Perry's description of the renewal of Self that the psyche can go through during psychosis. This description is found in his book *The Far Side of Madness*.) Almost all memory of my former self had disappeared. In fact, I could hardly read. I felt I had to relearn everything. I did not know who I was or where I was going. Later I found a birth certificate lying on the floor among the detritus of my life. There were three different dates on the certificate. I started wondering when I was really born, which naturally led to questions about who my parents really were and questions of whether I had been lied to about my birth and other parts of my life too. I realize now I was confusing the symbolic question, "What is my true Self?" with the literal question, "What is my real birthday?" (Later, when I had rejoined the world, I reexamined the birth certificate and could understand the reason for three different dates. The earliest date was my actual birth date. The next, two weeks later, was when the certificate was filed with the state. The last date, 1960, referred to the date the certificate was reissued so that I could travel to Canada to go canoeing. This example is an illustration of how people in severe emotional distress seek clues within their environment to explain who they are.)

I tried to read. I picked up a book but I could only make out the letters and could not process them to form words. I panicked. I walked to the bathroom where I saw my housemate Leon putting white stuff on his face and scraping it off.

"What are you doing?" I asked him.

"Shaving, of course," he replied, startled and frightened when he realized I did not know what shaving was.

We decided to go for a walk but the entire world seemed dead. There was a cold autumn breeze blowing leaves across the street. There were no leaves on the trees. We went to the corner restaurant, named The Empire, which I thought said "Vampire." I was sure that everyone there was actually dead. The complexion of everyone inside appeared to be a sallow yellow. It was as if my old world had died the night before. The world I had carefully constructed during the first twenty-five years of my life had disappeared and I did not yet have a new one to take its place. So I desperately attributed any meaning I could to what was happening, as if all of life happened outside of me. I could not feel any life inside me; I felt dead inside. I didn't like any of the food in the restaurant.

When I returned to our place, I yelled to Herbie, another roommate, "Go out and get me some food."

"What do you want?" he asked.

I had no idea. He said ice cream helped him when he was upset. I tried a little ice cream, but it didn't seem right. I lay motionless on the couch, afraid that any action would be the wrong action. So I just lay there and looked at the sunlight streaming through the few remaining leaves. For a short while it was beautiful and I felt uplifted. Then my hell began again. I found myself within a dream, which I confused with reality. I was many thousand years old. I turned on the television looking for answers to explain what was going on and who I was. I imagined that the Pope had a message with special meaning for me, and he spoke directly to me and only me. This made me feel significant and noticed. It also reflected my enduring need to have someone in a position of authority define who I was. I thought I was Albert Einstein. I rushed to the bookshelf and read parts of his biography. I became convinced that I had really written words attributed to him. Though still in a dream-like state, I then insisted that I had to talk with Dr. Jack Durell at NIMH. I was sure he could solve my problems. He seemed so sure of himself and held such an important position. A friend from the lab stopped by. He said nothing had happened at the lab since I had been away. I thought that meant that every discovery at the lab depended on me, which again fueled my sense that I was Einstein. This thought also revealed how I felt my actual life was insignificant.

These friends then decided to take me to Baltimore. As I looked up at the stars I imagined that they were the eyes of my ancestors looking down at me in disappointment. I felt I had let them down and not followed their instructions. I felt I was being returned to Baltimore to be reminded of my life instructions. I was very clever at listening to what people wanted me to hear and feeding that song back to them. I was the good son, unlike my older brother who had refused to do what was expected of him. I fulfilled my parents' dream and the family tradition, which was to be good at studies and baseball, and become a doctor.

I continued to look for an explanation to make sense of what was happening around me. I stayed with my sister, Sally, and searched for clues. She had a picture of London on the wall and I asked her where it came from; she said from our mother. I thought that meant that our mother was really the Queen of England. That would make me a prince. Then I felt I should not move, because if I made the wrong move something terrible would happen. So the safest position was to not move at all. I should not talk, as well. I could picture all my dead relatives in heaven with their jewels, directing the course of my life.

Understandably, my family, out of fear and lack of alternatives, took me to the psychiatric unit at Johns Hopkins Hospital. It was embarrassing to be there as a patient, as my father and brother-in-law were on the faculty. So I softened the blow by saying to myself that I was being brought there to be the head of the psychiatry department. (Though at the time I was experiencing these thoughts I didn't realize why they were occurring.) When they showed me my bed, I thought, "My, this is unusual for the head of psychiatry to sleep on the ward." The Donovan song, "Mellow Yellow," was playing in the background. I listened intently, trying to get a message from it as to what I should do next. Shortly, a nurse arrived and asked me whether I wanted to take "it" by mouth or injection. Without knowing what "it" was, I imagined she was referring to sex. I refused both types very strenuously. This prompted her to request physical assistance from the goon squad. Two strong young men tried to hold me so she could give me the injection. I fought furiously against their efforts, summoning all the wrestling skills I learned years earlier in school. After I subdued each of them, reinforcements were called in. They kept saying, "Don't struggle, it will make it much easier," which just made me fight against them more strenuously. The next thing I knew I was blacking out.

I awoke in a dream-like world. I could hear conversations. I could hear all the sounds of the hospital. I started to imagine I was a little baby being reborn. I could hear the staccato clicks of my mother's heels as she walked on the hospital's marble floor. I could also hear parts of her voice, but I was unable to open my eyes or clearly attend to the sounds.

After several days, I fully woke up and discovered that I had returned to everyday reality. I told myself that everything that had happened must have been because of that mescaline. If I hadn't taken it, none of this would have happened. So I assumed if I just stayed away from the mescaline nothing like that would happen again.

I decided I needed a new therapist, as the man I had been seeing was so remote that the analysis had not felt helpful. I interviewed a psychiatrist named George Semchyshyn and made one major request, "Could you be real?"

"I will try," he said, in a very genuine fashion.

We collaborated during three very productive years of therapy. He took an interpersonal view and kept seeing me in the most real and humanistic of ways. He was not easy to characterize. Whenever he would come up with a helpful insight, I would congratulate him. With genuine humility, he would quickly say that I produced the insight. He told me he merely provided the setting for me to arrive at new understandings.

Meanwhile, I returned to my job at the laboratory, but my heart was still not in it. Deep inside, I realized that I was going through a profound transition: I could not go back to being the person I had been previously. Yet I was still too frightened to move forward. My rolling stone life had come to a standstill, while inside I felt as if there was no Self to give me an idea of which direction I should take next. Breaking down my old self had left me feeling lonely and empty. "Like a rolling stone, no direction home, a complete unknown," as Bob Dylan sang. I needed purpose and I needed a tribe to work with towards that meaning.

Leon was an early member of my tribe. He had connected with me shortly after Sarah had left. His wife had left him too, and he called and suggested we go to a singles dance. That was a mistake, as the singles were largely middle-aged and we were much younger. Leon went to social work school and became a therapist. He introduced me to the Washington Free Clinic. He was also a good singer and guitar player. We did duets and our favorite song was "Your Song" by Elton John.

Some people thought we were gay because the song was about Elton John's lover.

Another member of my tribe was Jim. I met Jim while I was fighting air pollution. He was working for Ralph Nader and I was the volunteer technical director of the Metropolitan Washington Coalition for Clean Air. Until Jim joined, I was the only member of the technical committee. He and I created the Fisher-Sullivan guidelines for air pollution abatement in Washington, DC.

In the summer of 1970, I met a terrific architect. I hoped she would be the love of my life, as we seemed very compatible and connected on every level. We were going to go on a weeklong vacation with Leon and his girlfriend. Then, suddenly, I received a long letter from her explaining she had too many issues of her own and she had to leave. So Leon, his girlfriend, and I drove twelve hours up to Maine for the vacation. I felt like a third wheel. We smoked pot, but it only made me feel more out of place. I couldn't sleep, and after a week drove twelve hours back to Washington, convinced I was in Hades.

On my return, I withdrew again into the safety of the caverns of my mind. After several days of frightening images and fantastic imaginings, I retreated into silence. My neurochemical research seemed irrelevant. Why was I studying the chemistry of emotions when such impersonal research was not helping the personal pain I was experiencing? I called the lab to report that I did not feel I could go to work. I reached our secretary, Hattie. She was calm when I started to tell her that I was just too stressed to work.

"Why don't you go to the zoo, that is a lovely place to go if you are feeling stressed," she suggested. She was breaking away from the cold scientific world, too.

I spent a day alone at the zoo, feeling much too connected to the pain of the trapped and caged apes. I looked for a long period at a motionless lizard. I connected to the being of the lizard and this helped me feel less alone. I imagined I was the phenylalanine hydroxylase enzyme I had been studying in the lab. I could see the phenylalanine shooting towards me and I had to quickly add oxygen to it to form tyrosine to avoid injury.

On that cool August day in 1970, I stopped talking, eating, and moving. My friends were terrified. They contacted my psychiatrist, who told them to take me to Bethesda Naval Hospital. My friends jammed me into a car, which caused them major difficulty because I could not bend my body. They had to leave my legs sticking out of the car window. The police stopped them, wondering why my legs were sticking out of a window. I was dimly aware that this was happening but was no longer able to move my body. In great haste, they dropped me off with no identification and no possessions at the emergency room of the hospital.

Each ER professional approached me with a clipboard in hand and questions on their lips. What is your address? Who were the last five presidents in reverse order? Every question seemed like an attack. They really didn't seem to care whether I was there or not. There seemed no reason for me to respond. Gradually they gave up, put me in a wheelchair, and rolled me into a corner.

Eventually, a corpsman, the lowest-ranking member of the staff, stopped to be with me. Unlike the others, he displayed curiosity and interest. He looked directly into my eyes in a caring and steady fashion for what seemed an eternity. I was struck by the shining quality of his vision. His presence and caring intrigued me enough to return his gaze. He smiled for what seemed an eternity. He observed me in a very gentle, non-demanding fashion.

"You seem to be in a great deal of distress," he observed calmly.

He was the first person in some time who had taken the trouble to actually see the "me" inside.

"Hi, my name is Rick," he said in a genuine manner. He seemed to be a *real* person.

"Just nod if you can hear me," he entreated.

I nodded and felt there was a possibility of connecting with him. Then, I had a moment of authentic connection with Rick and entertained the possibility of returning to the everyday world. But abruptly I was wheeled onto the locked ward. My clothes, a yellow shirt with green stripes and a pair of green slacks, were taken from me never to be returned. I vainly tried to hold on to them. I felt that if I lost them I would lose the last shred of my identity. The loss of one's clothing combined with the labeling process is part of the degradation ceremony of institutionalization, which Irving Goffman referred to in *Asylums*.

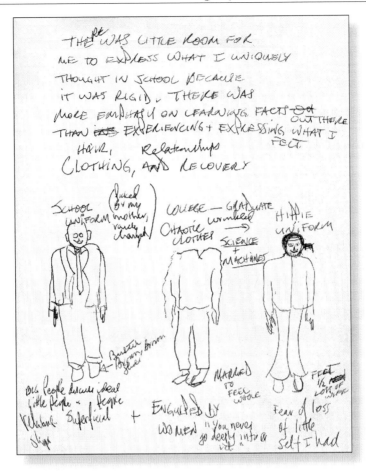

In the years since Sarah left, my clothing had become an expression of who I was. I dressed traditionally for the lab by day, but at night I adopted the garb of a hippie. My hippie outfits, with bell bottom pants and flowered shirts, conformed to the place and time I lived in, but they also represented a break from tradition. I would also wear a bandana and sandals or boots of various styles. I let my hair grow long, often placing it in a ponytail. I also grew as much beard as I could. The drawings above and on the facing page trace my life stages in terms of clothing. The first drawing reads: "... There was little room for me to express what I uniquely thought in school because it was rigid." There was more emphasis on learning facts out there than expressing and experiencing what I felt. I described the sequence as hair, relationships, clothing and

44

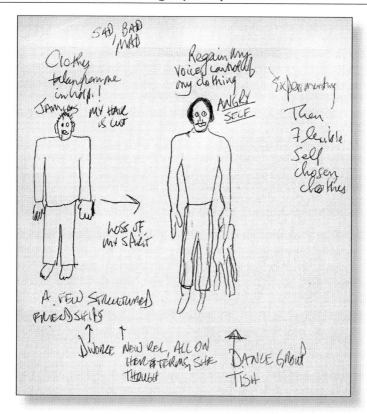

recovery. The theme is going from my prep school life of following the expectations of school and mother to finding my own Voice.

When I entered Bethesda Naval Hospital and they grabbed my clothes from me, I felt part of my spirit go with them. The hospital johnny I was forced to wear felt like an assault. I was never given back my clothes and I still can feel their loss. Several days later they insisted on cutting my hair. They said such long hair was against Navy regulations. I was not able to speak up, so they cut, and I cried as my locks fell in piles around me.

I am reminded of an early leader of our movement, Leonard Frank, who was hospitalized because he chose to live a beatnik life, which included long hair and beard. Similarly, a goal of Frank's treatment was to cut his hair and beard. They ultimately gave him so many shock treatments (ECT) that he could not resist. However, ever since his release he has donned a long, flowing mane and a distinguished, professorial beard. He dedicated the rest of his life to fighting ECT. His recent death was a great loss to our movement, though I carry him in my heart.

I stayed in a scared, nonverbal state for three weeks. I had trapped myself. I watched the expressions of each of the workers, trying to discern a reason to talk with them. I kept straining to recall any familiar trait to give me a clue as to who these people were. I was carrying around a book on nonverbal communication and the corpsmen read it.

Finally, another caring corpsman named John attempted to reach me. We developed our own sign language, which enabled us to communicate nonverbally. Gradually, over a three-week period, I felt I could trust him, and I began to believe again that talking was worthwhile. The nonverbal aspect of communication, which is probably based on our very first year in this world, needs to be firmly established to make life worth living, and the verbal dimension worthwhile. The nonverbal dimension of communication transmits most of our emotional life and sense of Self. When we can communicate well on this emotional level, we feel an inner unity and vitality. Later, I will elaborate on this phenomenon in describing eCPR (Chapter Eight).

I was given Thorazine during that period. I only recall that the medication had side effects. Much more fundamentally, engaging in a personal relationship was the essential element that led me to reconnect with the world. I often think back to those weeks and I now believe those corpsmen saved my life. Corpsmen were the least professionally trained and held the lowest status of all the members of the mental health team, yet they were surely the ones who were vital. I have observed similar situations a number of times during the years since I was at Bethesda Naval Hospital. There is something very wrong with our system of care if the least-trained, lowest-status members often provide the greatest help. This is an experience shared by most of us who have recovered. It seems that professional training and elevation in status tends to select out the qualities most essential for helping another human being through a crisis.

My doctor at the hospital was also very helpful reconnecting me to humanity. Dr. Kaplan was able to communicate real caring. An example was the day I could not get out of the shower. I just sat down on the floor of the shower and could not imagine any way of getting up. The shower was soothing my pain with its constant pressure of a thousand "fingers" on my back. Tech nurses tried to get me out but were embarrassed when facing the task of moving a nude adult out of the shower. I asked for my doctor. Soon Dr. Kaplan, in his white Navy uniform, was sitting on the floor of the shower next to me. He just looked at me for awhile and then nodded to the door.

"This is kinda of silly, and I am getting pretty wet. Don't you think it is time to get up from here?"

I followed him out. His caring manner was immediately apparent and he was not afraid to be himself and share his humanity.

During my hospitalization, I decided I needed to make changes in my life. I believed that this time my extreme emotional state had been brought on by losing my most recent girlfriend and from smoking grass. But on a deeper level, there were other reasons for going into the other reality.

I soon learned to play the game they wanted me to play at the hospital and I was given a pass to visit my lab across the road at the NIMH. I was delighted to taste freedom and I was asked how I felt upon my return. "On a scale of one to ten," I answered, "I feel like eleven."

The staff decided I was too excited and promptly locked me in the seclusion room. Only a tiny Plexiglas window in the heavy wooden door and a heavily screened window offered a glimpse of the world outside. I was terrified. I was sure that the staff would leave me there forever. My fears were fueled by the indifference that I could observe among the staff visible through the window. I pounded on the door but received no response. I longed for human contact, yet there was none. I slumped down on the cold marble floor, my spirit draining from me. I stared up at the single grated light bulb above me.

I vowed to myself that if I ever got out of seclusion, I would become a psychiatrist and ensure that no one else would be treated in this fashion. I would find a way to ensure that when someone was gripped by terror, those in charge of their care would reach out and make contact rather than secluding them within walls and using medication. I wanted to give back to the corpsmen who had dedicated their lives to saving people like me.

This has been my life-altering dream; the sense of meaning and purpose has stayed with me for forty-six years. That dream and sense of purpose is similar to what psychiatrist Dr. Victor Frankel described when he composed his thoughts on bits of paper while held in a Nazi concentration camp. He said that his dream of one day writing a book about his experience kept him going. Each time the guards would tear up his manuscript he would gather the pieces and hide them in his shoe.

I grew faint and stared longingly through the screened window to outside. I must escape I told myself. Then I imagined I was a blue bird and saw myself fly through the window. I blacked out. When I came to, I was on the ward and remembered my dream. I made the compromises I needed to make to get discharged.

By then I knew what types of changes I needed to make in my life. In my work life, I realized I needed to change careers. That realization was huge! I had invested so much of myself into being a neurochemist. The thought of leaving that career was so challenging that I had had to enter another reality to consider such a change.

Friends were critically helpful during my recovery. They helped me keep a grasp on the reality of my situation. One day, two housemates came to visit and brought a copy of Ken Kesey's novel *One Flew Over the Cuckoo's Nest*.

One friend remarked, "Man, this place is crazy. You gotta get outta here. We brought this book because you are like the character in the book — McMurphy. You gotta get outta here before they control you like they did McMurphy."

I saw they had a good point and was so relieved to get their outside perspective. I also knew I should not share this perspective with the hospital staff. The countercultural perspective of the '70s helped me to construct the new, fuller life I needed to recover my humanity.

Three months later, I was discharged on Haldol and handed a sheet of green paper. At the bottom of the page was the frightening word "schizophrenia." The word leapt off the page. It can't be true, I can't be *schizophrenic*. Was it possible? Had I been diagnosed with the same condition I had been studying across the Rockville Pike at the NIMH? The doctors had never told me what my diagnosis was while I was in the hospital. I was disheartened but not subdued.

Luckily, my friends, therapist, and family did not treat me as

if my life was over. I was very fortunate to have their love and support. Little statements can be very powerful. I also felt encouragement from my mother's gift, at the time, of a Currier and Ives print of Daniel in the Lion's Den. I identified with Daniel in the lion's den of the psychiatric hospital.

One day at Thanksgiving dinner, while sitting next to my sister-in-law, I admired how much she and my brother were in love. I told her I never thought I would have a successful relationship. In a sweet, reassuring, and sincere manner, she put her hand on my arm and said, "I know that someday you will make someone a very loving husband." For years to come, I held on to those words like the finest of gems, and eventually her prediction came true.

My therapist, George, also always believed in me. When I told him of my dream to go back to medical school and become a psychiatrist, he said he would be at my graduation. Indeed, six years later, he came to my graduation from George Washington Medical School. I interviewed George in 2011 to better understand how he helped me. Sadly, he died in 2014.

Conversation with Dr. George Semchyshyn, 2011

Thirty-five years after I last saw George Semchyshyn at my 1976 Medical School graduation, I met with him while writing this book. I found him on the Internet and visited his crowded office in Falls Church, Virginia. His hair, what was left of it, had turned salt and pepper grey. But his voice, smile, and manner were just as inviting as when I had first walked into his office forty-one years earlier.

The following is a summary of my conversations with George. I am sure there will be more and I think we will become friends.

Dan: What do you feel helped me recover?

George: I could see that you developed an observing ego. That ego allowed you to understand yourself better. I found that self-psychology helped me understand what you were going through.

Dan: What did you see in me?

George: I saw the healthy part of you. I could see that you were restructuring yourself. I see schizophrenia in stages. You improved after each episode of psychosis.

Dan: Where did you get the idea that I, or any one with schizophrenia, could recover without medication?

George: That understanding came from my experience in Vietnam. I became an army psychiatrist right after I finished my residency and was stationed in Vietnam. I saw soldiers with acute psychosis. I would snow them with a major tranquilizer and after several days they would clear. Then I had to decide in a short period who should return to combat and who should go home.

Dan: What did you see as a strength in me?

George: You were very likeable. You have personality factors that helped in your recovery.

Dan: How did you communicate with me when I was in other realities?

George: I always thought there was meaning in what you were saying. I also went to where you were. One time I could tell you felt too confined in your apartment, so I walked with you to DuPont Circle where we sat for a long time, mostly in silence.

Dan: What did you feel I was going through?

George: I felt you were going through regression in service of the ego.

At the end of our interview, I told George that I was disappointed that I never really learned what he was thinking during our therapy. I told him I came to him with a series of questions and felt we just ended up having a conversation. He laughed and said, "Don't you remember? That was the essence of our therapy. We engaged in conversation. That seemed the most helpful approach for you."

Here are some of the elements I felt were most helpful in my relationship with George:

- He always viewed me as a whole person.
- He helped me see the ways in which I was capable of coming to insights myself, and he respected my capacity to heal myself.
- He used a very personable, relaxed way of being that allowed me to trust him.
- In his use of conversation as his major tool, he was humble and authentic, so the conversation flowed easily.
- He seemed to freely use his spontaneous self, though remaining aware of his impact.
- He always believed in my capacity to recover and supported my dreams.

For two years, I worked every week at the Washington, D.C., Free Clinic, doing both individual and group peer support. I yearned to help people as I had been helped. By helping them through their distress, I came to understand more about myself. Often a person with a mental health diagnosis feels as if their ability to make a contribution is negated, but it is through sharing ourselves that we feel valuable and still connected to the human race.

Three years after my discharge from Bethesda Naval Hospital, I applied to several medical schools. I was accepted at George Washington University Medical School. However, the dean called and asked if I had ever been hospitalized psychiatrically. I was gripped with fear. Quickly I recovered and asked, "What made you ask that?" He told me that though I had a normal physical exam, my boss at NIMH had said I had been sick several times. So I admitted the truth. He said they would admit me if my psychiatrist would write a letter stating I was capable of attending. Luckily, George wrote such a letter. Today, no school could ask such a question as it would violate the Americans with Disabilities Act of 1990.

Medical school was not easy. However, I was fortunate to have had help from a cat named Nosey. Pets seem to sense when people are in need and, perhaps from some instinct to care for their young, they can provide emotional support in times of distress. Every day during my first year of medical school I would return to my apartment exhausted and near defeat. One day there was a cat in my apartment. Even though my doors were locked, a very friendly tiger cat had made herself welcome at my place. I realized it was Nosey, the cat who had run away when its upstairs owner moved. Perplexed, I put Nosey out only to find her there the next day. A neighbor pointed out to me that the cat had gotten into my apartment by walking along a narrow ledge and squeezing through the screen. So I adopted Nosey and she adopted me. She lay in my lap and purred each time I returned from school. She needed me like a kitten looking for milk. I grew attached.

In January 1974, I had a dream, which lit the way for the next aspect of my recovery. I call it the "Castle Dream." It became the most important vision for both my personal recovery and for a new way of seeing and assisting people through madness. I first shared the dream in a group therapy session led by clinical psychologist and author Sheldon Kopp. Here is the dream:

> I went to a castle and found that a colonel had two young corporals imprisoned in a dungeon against their will. Whenever the young men complained about their imprisonment, the colonel would give them a lecture on how crazy they were. He would bring out the drawing of a gargoyle on yellowing map-like material. He said they could not leave because their brains were deformed and looked like the gargoyle (see facing page). But the colonel's main weapon was the men's own ignorance about how they were originally imprisoned.

> I entered the dream as a lieutenant and was shocked by the imprisonment of these two normally appearing young men. I (in the form of a lieutenant) did some research and discovered that several years ago they had been doing laboratory research and had looked through a microscope too long. This caused a blind spot to develop in their brains. This blind spot had caused them to do scary, crazy things for which they had been imprisoned in the castle.

> Over time they were no longer locked in the castle, but the old colonel stood guard over them. The colonel's frequent lectures on their craziness prevented them from leaving the castle. He assured them that their condition was permanent — they would always be crazy. I learned that in fact the men's blind spot had long ago healed without any scarring

and they were healthy. They were no longer crazy. So I went to the colonel with the young men and presented the evidence I had uncovered. He got very excited and said it was nonsense. The two men and I started to walk out of the castle. When the old man tried to stop us, we brushed him aside and walked out into the sunlight.

A few days later I imagined the dream might have continued as follows:

The colonel picked himself up off the floor and caught up with the men. He asked if he could join them, complaining that it was very cold and lonely in the castle now that the young men had left. The lieutenant said it was fine but the two young men objected, as they wanted the colonel to suffer as they had. The three men conferred and decided to allow the colonel to accompany them if he shed his colonel's uniform. The two young men also wanted the lieutenant to shed his uniform, which he did. Then the four men marched, and then danced off with nothing in particular to do. They felt they had plenty of time to learn about each other and the strange new sights that surrounded them.

Here is how I described the next group therapy session in which I shared my dream:

Ten minutes before leaving my apartment for the group, I hurriedly copied over the dream for Shelly. All during my trip to the group I felt a tightness in my shoulders. I suspected the tightness was due to anxiety, and tried to define the thoughts that were causing my inner conflict. I sensed that I was trying to take the place of Bonnie in the group. During her three years in the group she had been the group's heart. She had given energy to the group by sharing her inner most thoughts and feelings with the group, and she had given Shelly material for the chapters in his books.

Now a week had passed since Bonnie had left and I found myself pulling my car into her old parking space, with my dream written out on a piece of paper for Shelly. I folded the paper several times so no one could notice that I was carrying it. I told Shelly I wanted to give him the dream as a gift, and as a way to help others who are struggling with problems similar to mine. But I also told him I felt used by his commercialization of my dream. Shelly said he was going to use my dream to make money and not to help people. My shoulders began to stiffen terribly.

Later I tried to offer assistance to another group member and swallowed the comment half-way through as the pain in my shoulders intensified and I realized that 90% of what I was saying was projection (i.e., my own story of the world). For some period I sat in silence aware only of the pain in my back when a thought came to me, which relieved the tension greatly. Excitedly I interjected, "I can't help anyone in this group. I can't help anyone and I don't think anyone can help me."

Shelly Kopp's eyes lit up and he shouted, "You're cured!" I walked out of the group dumbfounded and mumbled to myself that if he says that again I might leave. The thought of not being able to give my life meaning through therapy is frightening and gives me pain in my stomach. Well, at least that beats pain in my back. I'll bet some sweets would help the stomach feel less lonely. Besides, fear (a green emotion of passivity) beats anger (the red emotion of action). I was trying to classify emotions into categories based on colors they reminded me of. The thought of being cured is frightening to me because it means Shelly can no longer be my mother. That makes me lonely. Tonight I thought of showing my writings to Shelly so he could be an advocate for me, and I realize that is still trying to gain protection from him.

The dream reminds me of "Before the Law," a scene from Franz Kafka's *The Trial*. In the novel, Joseph K. wanders into a church where he hears a sermon about a man from the country who travels to the city to see the law. There is an open gate but a fierce guard watches over the gate. For years the man waits at the gate for the guard to say he can enter. Finally when he is very old, he asks the guard why no one else ever came to the gate and how he might have gained entrance. The guard said, "This gate was only meant for you. You could have entered if you had only asked. But you never asked, and now I am closing the gate." The dream reminded me that I could only progress in my life when I took initiative instead of waiting for authorities to give me permission.

I had this castle dream as I was nearing the end of a tempestuous three-year relationship with Sophie. One reason I was growing weary of Sophie was that she was in social work school and was reading textbooks about schizophrenia, from which she quoted devastating passages. For instance, she might look up from her book and remark, "It says here that people with schizophrenia never recover. I wonder if you will ever recover. They say that schizophrenia is hereditary. Does that mean that our children would likely develop it?"

In February 1974, Sophie and I went to a dance sponsored by Center for Science in the Public Interest to raise awareness about the need for alternative energy sources. (The center was started by my friend, Jim.) Sophie did not want to dance, so I scanned the dance floor and saw a cute young woman in a brown turtleneck. We kicked up our heels and I wanted to know more about her. She told me her name was Tish but I had to quickly say good-bye. Out of the corner of my eye I could see Sophie steaming across the floor towards us, despite Jim's attempts to slow her down. Later that week I asked Jim to look up Tish on the list of attendees but, alas, he could not find her on the list. My relationship with Sophie ended soon thereafter, and again I felt utterly alone. I isolated myself in my room and started writing day and night.

With prolonged isolation, my imagination again took off. I literally believed that everyone I knew had been replaced with a robot. I suspected I was the only human being left. I became convinced that we were all machines. Again, I went deep inside. My sister Sally came to be with me and tried nobly to reach me, as did my friend Jim. But I stayed stubbornly inside my world. I had become convinced that I should only drink organic apple juice and that eating would interfere with my insight. So, Sally should not have been surprised when she opened my fridge and found only 10 quart-bottles of apple juice.

One day when Sally and I were walking around the block, she noted that she felt as if she was walking on eggshells. Once again I was convinced that the entire world was dying. I tried to pull a cross from a woman's neck, thinking I would bring her back to life in that manner. Several police officers apprehended me. Luckily, a friend, Sandy, was there, and assisted by helping me calm down and get into the police car without a fight. I was taken to a police precinct where I literally lay on the ground, silent. When they learned that I was a medical student they sent me to a psychiatric hospital in a paddy wagon. The ride was made bearable by Sally thoughtfully placing her black coat over me. I needed a safe place and in the absence of any alternative, I was hospitalized in Sibley Memorial Hospital.

As an extension of my mechanized view of life, I became convinced that my emotional problems had been caused by permanent organic damage to my brain. When I was hospitalized, I believed I was being returned to the castle of fear and placed under the colonel's influence. I was ready to abandon all hope of recovery.

Luckily, Dr. Semchyshyn reappeared and continued to believe in my capacity to heal. In that dark hour, I was distraught and told him, "I must be permanently defective. I must have a biological brain disorder that will never heal. What other explanation could there be for why I am back in a psychiatric hospital for the third time? This is three strikes, and I am out."

I pleaded with Dr. Semchyshyn to tell me what was wrong. "Would I be this way the rest of my life?"

In his very calm and heartfelt way, Dr. Semchyshyn said, "No, I do not think that your problems are organic. I still believe that you can heal."

This simple yet profound statement by Dr. Semchyshyn was liberating. For me, the concept that my problems are primarily human and not organically based has been a source of a personal faith and trust in my capacity to confront any fear. This faith has given me the hope and

the courage to struggle, to continue, and to recover. I later describe this emergence of hope as saying "yes" to life.

He also demonstrated his trust in my capacity to face my problems by releasing me before I was fully cooperating with the staff. He helped me keep hope alive until I could hope for myself again. This hope evolved from the trust that had developed between us.

Leaving Sibley was extremely important. I began the process of finding my genuine Voice in that hospital. It seemed I had to enact the "Castle Dream" to undo the years of feeling trapped in my inner dungeon by the fears of my childhood. The staff did not believe I was ready for group therapy but I thought I was. In reaction to their decision, I passed around the ward a petition in support of my attending group therapy. Most of the patients signed the petition. However, when I presented it to the head nurse, she said I could not attend the group. I got angry and made the fatal mistake of raising my voice. She cautioned me to lower my voice.

"If I can't get angry in a mental hospital, where can I get angry?" I asked.

She ordered five strong men to "escort" me into seclusion. However, this time I was not going to let my spirit be ripped from me as it had been at the Naval Hospital four years earlier.

"He jumped so high..." I could hear strains of "Mr. Bojangles" filtering through the thick seclusion door. I peeked through the four-inch Plexiglas window. Jerry, another inmate, was playing his guitar and singing, "almost touched the sky..." He caught my eye and we shared a strengthening gaze. I took off my shirt so I could feel my strength more directly. I felt my Voice and I started to yell. I realized that the quiet room could be a very loud room if I kept my Voice and used it. I was not going to let them break my spirit and quiet me this time. I demanded to see my psychiatrist. Then I meditated for a few minutes to be sure I kept my center. I banged on the door and meditated some more.

Eventually, Dr. Semchyshyn appeared. He agreed to release me if I would put on my shirt. I agreed, though I said I would put it on later. He opened the door of the seclusion room and had them release me from the hospital. When I got to the lobby, I put on my shirt. Years later I asked him how he felt he could take such a risk. He said he was able to connect with me. When he looked out the window and he saw me walking away from the hospital with my shirt on, he was confident I could make it

It was a four-mile walk home and I savored every free step. I could smell the April flowers and felt the grass under my feet. I knocked on my downstairs neighbor's door. She took me into her apartment. I did not know her very well but I felt she had a good heart. She cradled my head on her lap and gently rocked me back and forth. She gave me honey and herbal tea. She didn't require an explanation of what had happened; she just was her warm self. Her presence and caring were like a salve to my wounded psyche.

I put on the rough orange poncho my brother had brought me from Colombia and braved the brisk morning air in DuPont Circle. As I walked, and then ran, around the fountain, it seemed as if I could feel blood returning to parts of my body I had cut off years before. I felt as if I had been out of touch with the inner me. I had been traveling in my mind to remote lands of great importance, but now I needed to get back in touch with my inner Self. Just prior to my hospitalization I had had a dream in which my apartment was a spaceship and I was a long way from earth. This indicated just how out of touch I had felt.

I walked over to Jim's Center for Science in the Public Interest. I had not seen him for a couple of weeks. and tried to explain what had been going on. Then I said I had to rest, so I lay down on the floor. I overheard someone ask, "Why is that person lying on the floor?"

"He's a friend of Jim's," was the reply.

That cleared me. Later I asked for some mindless task, and someone gave me envelopes to stuff. I started talking with one of the staff about the need to destroy all telephone lines in Washington. I wondered if we could put together a team of commandos to spread out through the city and simultaneous cut all communication wires, so that people could get back to face-to-face communication.

I returned to my apartment and was greeted by Nosey, who had somehow survived the two weeks while I was away. Night fell hard. My muscles were twitching from Thorazine withdrawal since I had left the hospital without meds or a 'script. I had no intention to start the meds again. My mind was twitching, too.

I spent six painful days not sleeping and not sure of the future.

One night I was sure I needed to end my life. I lay in the bathtub in despair. I thought to myself, "What possible reason do I have to continue living?" Two thoughts kept me alive. First, I was curious as to what would happen next. It still seemed that something new and unexpected might happen. This meant I could let go of the conviction that I had no future. Second, and even more fervently, I said to myself, "I can't kill myself. Otherwise, who would take care of Nosey?" I couldn't think of anyone else. I decided I had to go on living to take care of the cat who had adopted me.

I said to myself, "I am going to say 'yes' to life." Later I realized I must have been saying "no" to life for a long time prior to that. Yes, life was worth living. I think a large part of experiencing my humanity

59

has been saying "yes" to life. Freud would say I went from Thantos to Eros. I was experiencing my deepest spirit, which had left me and now was back. It seems I had to reach inside to my most essential level of life and death to rediscover my deepest spirit. That seems to be the moment when my maelstrom of despair turned into a hurricane of hope (see illustration above). I felt like Dorothy in *The Wizard of Oz*, kicking the heels of her ruby red slippers and saying, "There is no place like home." I felt I could return myself to the home inside myself, the home of my spirit. That was when I said goodbye to my raven self and hello to my heron Self.

On another sleepless night, I called my brother-in-law because I was concerned I was having a heart attack. Like a typical medical student, I was monitoring my heart rate. It was averaging 140. Chuck talked me through the crisis over the next two hours in the most soothing manner. First he addressed my medical concern. When I told him my heart rate, he said I didn't need to worry, because peoples' heart rate regularly rises above that when they are having sex. Then he just started asking me a series of questions about day-to-day matters. Where was my uncle? How was my mother doing? At one point I asked why he was asking such obvious questions. He said that this is what he learned was helpful when someone was in acute distress. His conversation that night was a lifeline. After six nights off the Thorazine and after six nights of not sleeping, I finally followed Chuck's advice regarding the medication. He said just take one pill and get a night's sleep and call him in the morning. I took a single Haldol, slept for a night, and needed no further meds.

THREE

Living My Life in Harmony with Others

In this last phase of my life, which I call my heron phase, I feel my life is taking flight. I call this phase living in polyphony. According to Russian philosopher Bakhtin, polyphony means learning to live life in the present moment by accepting the unfolding of a variety of points of view. I never fully believed in the description of my emotional challenges as they had been commonly portrayed by the psychiatric field, and it was fortunate that I was surrounded by others who were equally skeptical. In the period following my third hospitalization, I came to realize that my problems were not permanent. I rejected the idea that I, or anyone diagnosed with mental illness, had a condition that was primarily caused by a brain disorder. **Rather it makes more sense to understand that the problems described as "mental illness" are actually due to traumas which interfere with interpersonal/emotional development.** Seven years after my last hospitalization I had the following dream and meditation, that helped me understand the connection between my extreme emotional states and my traumas:

> *I am back in Gilman School and many of my old teachers are there. They all have white hair and are frozen in various positions. Mr. Pine is leaning over a waste can about to vomit. He asks for some water, but I deny him water because he is too covered in chalk dust.*

As I awoke, I was struck by how similar the scene was to my "Castle Dream," which allowed me to connect Gilman School with the dungeon in which I felt trapped in the dream. Indeed, the teachers all seemed to be institutionalized and in a trance, like the old colonel in the earlier dream. I then recalled how my sixth grade teacher called me the corporal, because I used to wear a shirt with the corporal stripes. He had quite an impact on me. He always advised me to start over on a fresh piece of paper if ever I made a mistake because paper was cheap. He was also a friend of my father's. They were both taught math by the dreaded Mr. Morrow, whom my father feared. My father said that a classmate of his quickly completed his homework assignment and ended it with the math designation QED, which the student boastingly said meant "quickest ever delivered." However Mr. Morrow immediately tore up the paper and said, "Quickest Ever Destroyed!" Gilman was a school where it was important that you learned to know your place.

Years later, while meditating on this striking "Castle Dream," I connected my experience of psychosis with earlier trauma. In my meditation, I focused my attention on the picture of the gargoyle. The paper was old and yellow and the edges of the picture were frayed. I knew I had seen that paper before. I could see the faint features of a map behind the intimidating figure of the gargoyle. Suddenly it occurred to me that the gargoyle was superimposed on a map that had hung in my fifth grade room at Gilman. It was a frayed, yellowed map of the world. I was then struck by the memory that I was sexually abused by a fifth grade teacher. In fact, the basement to which he took me and the other children was referred to as "the dungeon." Also I recalled that I used to wear the khaki shirt with the corporal stripes sewed on the sleeve when I was taken to the basement. The fear those experiences etched in my soul had burned on until they were freed by my breakdown, breakthrough, dream, and meditation. I was whole — not broken — in my "Castle Dream." That dream had helped me imagine a way out of the dungeon of fear I had lived in for twenty years. But it still seemed that I had had to live out the dream in my conscious waking life in the extreme emotional state leading to my third hospitalization to become truly a free flying heron.

During the months following my third hospitalization, I started a new self-help program of my own design. I realized that for much of my life I had been looking for a romantic relationship to supply what I sensed was missing inside. I was looking for the completion of my emotional Self that I believed I could never provide myself. I remember that when I met Sarah I thought, "She can express her emotions so I won't need to." I was looking for mothering. This was a very risky way to operate. It explained why, when Sarah left, I felt I was but half a person. It also explained why I had always felt under the control of any woman I was involved with. I knew that if I lost them I would be lost. So I decided to be less dependent on a female companion. I would need to mother myself. I focused on cooking. If I could become a better cook, I would be able to feed myself, both literally and figuratively.

Friends played a pivotal role in my recovery. During a dark hour in medical school, I realized I needed both the support of friends and some fun activities in my life. I found a square-dancing group and made some dear friends, some of whom I am still close to four decades later. I was always shy by nature and the rhythm of dance made meeting friends easier. Though peer support is important, friendship and love relationships are even more valuable.

Several months later, Leon and I were walking home from our favorite restaurant. Coming the other way were two young women, engrossed in conversation. One of them looked familiar. I smiled in recognition and she smiled back. We walked past each other, but then I turned and said, "Wait a minute, I know you." We soon established that we had met at the dance for alternative energy and that her name was Tish. I admitted I had asked my friend to find her name on the list. She revealed that her name didn't appear on the list as Tish because she had signed in with her full name, Letitia. She said she and her friend were looking for an apartment in the area. I told her I knew of one. (I really thought I did, though it did not turn out to be available. To this day she says I must have used the possibility of an apartment as a ploy.) She gave me her phone number and said, "Call me if the apartment is available, or just call anyway." She saw something in me, as she had never previously given out her number to a man she barely knew. Soon we were dating and more.

After several dates, I invited Tish to my apartment for dinner. I was planning to make split-pea soup, pasta and sauce, and salad. Unfortunately my timing was off. I overcooked the soup and the pasta. Tish, however, was touched that I made the effort. She was also impressed that I was making shelves for my books — one of my only construction jobs. In later years, if she wanted something fixed around the house she would say how I had fooled her with building those shelves. "I thought you were going to be handy like my father." Mostly those jabs were in good fun, a sign of her Irish humor, which still catches me off guard.

After a year, Tish and I went on a canoe trip together in the Maine woods. On our last night out, we met a spooky man who lived alone and regulated the dam on a lake. It was getting dark and we asked if there was a campsite nearby. He pointed to a nearby island and said it was a very good site. He then added in an eerie tone, "You will be perfectly safe there, no one would ever bother you." Later that night, as the wind rustled our tarp, we started getting frightened. Something about the way the man said you will be perfectly safe made us both worry that he might want to harm us. We held each other tightly but barely slept. At the end of the long drive back, I was getting frightened and my old feelings of paranoia returned.

I tried attending medical school, but foolishly I pulled out my musical wind instrument, a recorder, and played a few notes in a class.

I felt myself slipping into the familiar state of not moving or talking, because both felt unsafe. For long periods I stared at the ceiling, trying to understand questions I could not articulate. Tish was very worried about me as she had never seen me in such a state. The most helpful support she received was from Tom, a friend from my research days at NIMH. He had seen me go through two previous periods of psychosis. Tom and I had camped and canoed together during the previous four years. Tish and I went to visit him while I was in this altered state. He served us blueberries and cream. I tried to eat them one by one with a skewer. Tish shared her concern with Tom; she wondered if I would get through this period.

"Don't worry. I have seen him go through these states before and he always comes out stronger than when he started," he assured her.

She stuck with me day and night for three days. I came through — and do believe Tom was right. I felt even stronger. I went through the experience with taking just one Haldol and I think that by facing my devils, with a lot of help from my friends, I was able to come to terms with my fears. I have never had another episode of similar magnitude.

The other close call was three months later, during the winter of 1975. Tish and I were spending a month in San Francisco while I did a child psychiatry rotation. I was reading Robert Heinlein's novel, *Time Enough for Love*. At one point, the protagonist's computer starts to show human emotions such as jealousy. Once again, I found the blurring of the line between man and machine greatly troubling. Tish and I were able to talk it through and I took one milligram of Haldol. That was the last time I took a major tranquilizer. I do not believe one has to be off all medications to show complete recovery. However, the fact that many of us have recovered from schizophrenia and no longer need any medication is evidence that these conditions are not permanent biological brain disorders. I believe that going through the psychosis together with Tish solidified our relationship. By finding that she could stick with me even in my craziest state, I learned that I could trust her deeply.

Even after living together for five years, we were both wary of marriage. So we approached marriage in reverse. First, we bought a house together, then we went on a honeymoon to the South Pacific. Finally, seeing we could love each other even more deeply through all those experiences, we married in 1979. Recently, I asked Tish why she stayed with me, despite my having gone through such extreme emotional states. She said she had always believed in me, and in my capacity to grow and become strong. She never thought of me as defective or sick. She carried a bucket of hope when mine was in short supply. Our support is mutual, as she has also relied on me.

In addition to my relationship with Tish, I instinctively knew that I would need the support of persons with lived experience of recovery to get through my residency in psychiatry. As I neared the end of medical school, I sought a residency near such a peer support group. Fortunately, I was accepted at the psychiatric residency program located at Cambridge Hospital, a Harvard teaching hospital in Cambridge, Massachusetts. I knew, from reading a newspaper called *Madness Network News*, published by persons with lived experience, that the advocacy group, Mental Patient's Liberation Front (MPLF), was also in the Cambridge area. So, before I arrived, I wrote MPLF, telling them I was an ex-patient (the designation of that time) and would be starting a psychiatric residency in a few months. I soon received a postcard from the group, which read, "You can attend our group as an ex-patient but not as a psychiatric resident." That postcard sat on my desk for a long time. I stared at it and tried to imagine how I could go to a meeting as only half of myself.

Eventually I learned that the leaders of MPLF had formed a new group for people in dual roles, such as myself. They called the group Friends of MPLF. That group was invaluable in sustaining me in my struggle to chart a course through the dangerous waters of being an undisclosed person who was labeled with "mental illness" while also being taught to label others. It was also through that group that I met others with lived experience of recovery who had gone on to have children. Their example gave me hope that one day I could have children of my own. And, when I moved to Boston to start my residency, I found an excellent therapist named Jeff through a radical therapy network,

Another bridge to MPLF formed on the day someone I was serving asked me to look inside a form she handed me. There I found a flier for a book entitled *On Our Own*. The woman said, "The author is a friend of mine and she would like to meet you." The author was Judi Chamberlin, and in that year, 1978, she would change my life forever. Judi was one of the leaders of MPLF. Her passion for liberation, forged through her own lived experience, lit the way for me and other advocates around the world for the next thirty-three years. It still does.

The transition in two years from being involuntarily locked-up in seclusion in a hospital to being a psychiatrist writing orders for other patients was difficult to navigate. As I mentioned, the peers of the Cambridge MPLF were not ready to accept me; I was mistrusted because of my psychiatric training. At the same time, I did not disclose my psychiatric past to the training program at Cambridge Hospital, though I believe they could tell on occasion that I was struggling.

I can envision myself as a blue heron flying gracefully, overcoming gravity and the wind. So, too, I had to overcome and transform my anger into passion and vitality. I had launched myself, largely out of the fury I felt at the psychiatric system. Yet there I was, one of the oppressors working within the system that was the focus of my criticism. In addition, I was angry when I realized that important lessons I had learned during my recovery were in conflict with how the psychiatric hospital routinely carried out its treatments. For instance, I had learned from my own intense personal experience that no matter how extreme a person's emotional distress might be, there is always a person inside who can be reached. That person may outwardly appear to be mute, yet within he is watching and listening to every word and every intonation spoken by people surrounding him. He is especially attuned to the emotional tone of those around him. Establishing trust is crucial to reaching that person inside. Forcing medication against someone's will only ruptures a sense of trust.

My experience with a person with lived experience, Ms. Crosby, sorely tested my ability to balance between the lessons I had learned during my recovery and what I was told to do during in my residency. I was working in the emergency room during the first year of my residency when the call came in that Ms. Crosby had thrown a television through the window of her house. The crisis team said she needed to be hospitalized. I went to her home with the ambulance. I had been Ms. Crosby's psychiatrist during her previous hospitalization so I felt I might be able to reach her. She was brought out to the ambulance to be strapped into the transport chair. She was not speaking and I could clearly see the fear in her eyes. But I could also sense the hidden person inside. I tried to calm her and talked to her about how we would do all we could to help her.

I explained slowly what the process would be. When we got to the emergency room, she was not talking and refused to take medication, so the staff wanted to transfer her to the state hospital. I was able to communicate with her by just asking her to nod "yes" or "no," calling upon my own experience of having been in a mute state. I asked her if she could promise not to hurt herself or anyone else. She nodded in agreement. I said I would admit her to a voluntary unit at the general hospital.

When I admitted her to the unit, the staff was horrified. They couldn't understand why I had admitted a person in a state of catatonic psychosis and why I had promised her I would not medicate her if she agreed she would not harm herself or anyone else. The staff was too frightened to bring her meals or draw her blood, so I had to do so. My supervisor ordered me to medicate her. He confronted me repeatedly during morning rounds.

"Why are you not medicating this patient?" he demanded.

I replied that I was building trust.

He laughed and led the rest of the staff in laughter. "Dr. Fisher is building trust with a psychotic patient! That is ridiculous. The treatment of choice is 400 milligrams of Thorazine."

After several days, though, I had made great progress in reaching the mute woman through nonverbal communication. However, on the fifth day, my supervisor was fed up and called the assistant director of the department. I backed down when it appeared I would be terminated from the training program. Ms. Crosby was forcibly medicated. Upon discharge, she thanked me for the several days I had spent reaching out to her and building trust before she was medicated. She had very few hospitalizations after that.

I am amazed I made it through my residency. There were vast philosophical differences between my view of people with lived experience and that of the chief of staff. I detested reading peoples' charts; they were demeaning and dehumanizing. Instead, I preferred to get to know the person firsthand before I read his or her chart. Then, when giving presentations at rounds I would describe my impressions of the person based on my observations of them as a whole person. On one such occasion, when I admitted to the staff that I would not read a chart until I had conducted several interviews, the chief said I was being irresponsible. We had a heated one-on-one exchange and again I could see I was very close to being kicked out of the training program. So I made a few concessions.

During my practice as a psychiatrist, I have gradually been able to find words for those wordless states that others and I go through during emotional distress. I have always felt that there is a strong core of strength hiding inside each person, no matter how deeply upset they may be. I refer to that strong, powerful core as the person's true Self. I find it essential to always remember that, no matter how distressed a person may be, their powerful, core, true Self is always there. When I am helping someone through a perilous time, I always try to be with the person in a manner that conveys confidence that they can draw on that hidden strength within themselves. This perspective has greatly helped in my work on eCPR, as described in Chapter Eight.

Often I wanted to disclose that the source of my knowledge came from my own experience, but I realized it would not be safe to do so while I was a resident. Several months after I had completed my residency, I was asked to be on a local Boston television talk show, "People are Talking," to debate the issue of forced treatment. Judi Chamberlin was also scheduled to be on the program. I was asked if the broadcast could also include a psychiatrist who would represent a "pro-coercion" point of view. The one I knew best was my former chief of staff. As we were getting ready to go on the air, I told him I was going to disclose that I had been psychiatrically hospitalized on several occasions prior to my residency. He said, "It is now fashionable to have been hospitalized." His words and dismissive manner infuriated me and I wanted to lash out at him with all the resentment I had bottled up during my residency. Instead, I thought of the larger cause of furthering the rights of everyone labeled with mental health conditions and transformed my anger to passion to carry on with my advocacy and the show.

Gradually I accepted that I could be a psychiatrist *and* retain my humanity. I feel that I gained this acceptance by filling out my life and sense of Self beyond my work. Having a family and friends means I am a human being who carries out psychiatry in addition to a having a variety of other dimensions.

My most important life work has been in assisting my wife in the nurturing of our children's growth into healthy adults. From the moment my older daughter, Caitlin, was born in 1982, to this moment, our most important concern has always been the growth and development of our two children. Being so connected with them has made it difficult for me to witness them travel off to pursue the dreams they have chosen to follow. When Caitlin graduated from college, she decided to travel to a small town in Brazil to pursue her dream of playing professional soccer. I gave her a print of a white heron I had photographed in Mexico ten years earlier. The heron is flying in front of a grove of mangroves whose roots are exposed above the water. I said I hoped we had given her the wings and roots needed to make such a journey. She said we had. I apologized for crying and she hugged me and said it was "perfect." She spent a very fulfilling year-and-a-half in Brazil.

A few years ago, I was reflecting on my years of parenthood with my younger daughter, Lauren. She had come on Father's Day to have lunch with me. We were looking out on our backyard, where we had celebrated many birthdays for our children. I told her we had always tried to do the best we could to help them grow into happy, fulfilled people. She held my hand and said she had felt that we gave them the best gift any parent could give. She said we helped her to become the Self she wanted to be. Though both my daughters are choosing unconventional paths, they are pursuing their dreams and seem happy doing so. They may not make a great deal of money or rise to positions of power and prestige, but I believe in them and they believe in themselves.

My other life's work is at the National Empowerment Center (NEC), which I co-founded 25 years ago with Judi Chamberlin, Pat Deegan, and Laurie Ahern. That work resulted in my selection to be a member of the President's New Freedom Commission for Mental Health. Through my role on that commission, I was able to infuse the concept of "recovery" into the national conversation about mental health. I see my role as a bridge between the world of the consumer/survivor movement and the world of the conventional mental health system. Through my credibility in both realms, I've been able to help people in each world understand each other.

My recovery from "schizophrenia" was a transformative spiritual evolution, from a compliant, dutiful son whose main mission was to cure his family, to a Self-aware, Self-directed adult. I had to break down in order to break through. I had to overcome my fear of getting to know people and letting them get to know me. Connecting at an emotional and spiritual level with others has been an essential aspect of this evolution. I feel my spirit grow stronger and can more readily express my emotions, passions, and likes and dislikes. Through those preferences, I understand who I am and what is most important to me. By understanding and accepting myself, I have found meaning that gives me a reason for being here. The more comfortable I am being myself, the more comfortable I am with other people being themselves. I can listen more deeply and not feel threatened that I will lose who I am in them. Neither do I feel a need to change them to be more like me. Like the children's song, "Free to Be . . . You and Me."

In May 2011, I was interviewed on Icelandic television. The following transcript of the interview neatly summarizes my thinking on my lived experience of recovery:

Q(uestion by interviewer): How did you recover?

A(nswer by me): I had people around me who always believed in me. I run a center called the National Empowerment Center. Our center's main mission is to bring hope to people. I always had people around me who believed I could recover: my family, my friends, and my therapist. It was the early '70s and there was optimism about difficulties. There was a sense that people had rights. So even though I was hospitalized, my family and friends all felt that I had rights.

My dream was to become a psychiatrist, to get the keys and let everyone out of psychiatric hospitals and help with their recovery. Luckily, I had a therapist who said, "Yes, I believe you can do it."

Q: But the consensus is that people do not recover from schizophrenia.

A: That is the general belief, but it is not founded upon fact. It is not the evidence. Those of us who have recovered, we are the evidence that people can and do recover. But when many people recover, they slide back into society. They don't want to talk about it because there is still stigma and discrimination.

Q: You must have confronted prejudice?

A: I want the world to know that no matter how serious your problem, there is a healthy person deep down, and that person can guide your own recovery, if the people around you, and you yourself can call that person forth.

Q: What is the key to that?

A: The key is finding that healthy core inside, finding it inside yourself and finding it in another person. I know when I am helping a person. I know when I am getting close to their core because a sparkle comes back to their eye, a smile, and vitality. We call it the person's vital center or sense of Self. In fact we have developed a program called Emotional CPR: **C**onnect, em**P**ower, **R**evitalize.

Q: By empower you mean use the strength of everyone to help them progress?

A: People need to gain their own Voice and be able to speak from their center. When they do so, they are not troubled by external voices nearly as much. One of the hallmarks of schizophrenia is hearing troubling thoughts or voices. I had troubling thoughts, but have not had them since I gained a Voice. Like an artist's Voice, it is what you are uniquely.

Q: How do you feel the system needs to change?

A: The system is too fixated on biology and medication. I originally was a biochemist. I worked on serotonin and dopamine at our NIMH. I know we have chemistry. You and I are talking, and there is chemistry, especially if there is a spark, a connection. But that is secondary to who we are. The pill will help temporarily. I am not opposed to medication, but it is overemphasized and if people believe that the pill will fix them, they just take the pill and won't do anything else. As a client of mine once said, "Medication gives me a foundation, but I build the house." The house of our life. You have to be the artist of your life. We are all artists at heart and we build our house.

Recovery we see as a future for everyone, as a vision. We put that out

72

there as a goal, as a hope, and as a belief. If this is accepted then our policies shift from maintenance, which they are now, just reducing symptoms, to actually living a full life in society, following dreams, having meaningful relationships, having meaningful work. That is really what we hope for.

Q: You emphasize the role of hope.

A: I say giving hope is better than giving false hopelessness, which is what our system is giving people now. When a young person comes in they are often told, "Just live a reduced life, don't expect a lot of your life." This makes people suicidal because hope is what people need.

My mother died several years ago at the age of ninety-eight. She had always wanted me to write a book about my life and recovery. She was a believer in words; in fact, I have volumes of her diaries. Her dying was a very intimate period for me: I felt I needed to be with her in her final days as she had been there at my birth. It seems our passage out of this life is similar to our passage into it. The mystery wrapped in an enigma that is life reveals a little more of itself during such peak experiences.

Though my mother had been slipping for several years, she maintained a strong spirit. Each morning she still fixed her hair, put on makeup, and came down to hold court in her dining room. She would often stay downstairs until ten at night, sorting through thousands of old pictures and showing them to her constant companions, Femi and Heather. Jay, who for thirty years was her secretary and much more, came to the house three days a week. Though his own health was failing, he never failed to be at her side.

Gradually, during my mother's early nineties, as she retired from her housing-restoration business, her relationship with Jay changed. He went from keeping track of her bills and transactions to becoming her personal care assistant. He made the shift effortlessly. One constant in those thirty years was their constant bickering. At times I would break up arguments that reminded me of two children squabbling. With some regularity she would fire him, then hire him back. At times, Jay would stand a little too close for her comfort. She would sternly say, "You are too close, get away." He would then quietly, patiently go back to his office and await her summons. "Jay, Jay, where are you?" she would soon call. So, on his last day in service to her, I should not have been surprised that she would not say goodbye. I pleaded with her, but she resolutely looked away. Although she knew he had a bad heart, I think she was too angry that he was leaving to say goodbye.

The next week she would not call him, nor he her. I called her and asked if she had called. She hadn't. I said it might help her if she would call him. She said, "It might help him, but it wouldn't help me." Finally, her trusted companion, Femi, was able to connect the two of them one last time by phone. We were all saddened when we heard that Jay died suddenly a few days later at the age of eighty-nine. His son said that without the job of taking care of my mother, Jay felt he had no purpose. One day he drove to the Unitarian Church that he and my mother had founded in Towson and entrusted his carefully crafted memorial service to the minister. That evening he died at home.

All of us involved in her care noticed that after Jay died, my mother stayed in bed much longer. Some mornings she did not come downstairs at all. She needed more and more assistance to get out of bed and would often want to go back to bed early. She seemed to lose her interest in living. One day, in early October, she was too weak to get out of bed. She seemed to have had a mild fever so her doctor admitted her to a local hospital. Other than the fever and some congestion, all her lab tests and her physical indicated everything was normal.

On the day of Jay's memorial service, Sally and I visited her in the hospital. She seemed scared and held the sides of the bed very tightly. She said she could not move her legs but when we assisted her, she could move them and even walk. The hospital wanted to keep her for rehabilitation. She made it clear to us, however, that she wanted out of the hospital. Repeatedly, she said she wanted to be home. For the next several days, whenever I called she would complain about the food and say she had to go home. So I brought her home, and she was delighted to be back. She awoke in the night and came to my room. She seemed disoriented. I asked her if she knew who I was.

"You are a close relative," she slyly responded.

"Actually you are my mother," I tried to orient her.

She retorted, "You are my mother."

How right she was. In those final days I had become her mother. Perhaps, by assuming that role, I helped her move out of this world.

Maybe I was helping her complete the cycle of her life and leave as she had entered this world. She could again experience the immediacy of experience with which we enter the world. By being in the present moment, it may have been easier for her to let go of her hold on life.

Over the next two weeks she made sporadic progress attempting to walk. But, once again, she started to stay in her bed. I called her from Texas where I had given a speech to parents of young people with mental health issues. She was happy to hear that I was giving them some hope. She also asked how many people were at the meeting, as she always wanted me to reach large numbers of people. On Halloween, one of her companions called. She was very concerned that my mother could not hold down food or liquids. The doctor visited and did blood work. The next evening, I spoke with the doctor and he informed me that my mother's kidneys had shut down. He estimated she only had two or three days to live.

I flew to Baltimore and could see she was in critical condition. She was still unable to swallow liquids and was slipping in and out of consciousness. I quickly alerted my siblings, wife, daughters, nieces, and nephews. They soon arrived and that afternoon was magical. Mom always responded very enthusiastically when surrounded by younger members of the family and that day was no exception. She woke up and spoke to my daughters, telling them they were good girls. Lauren had been out climbing a tree, and had scratched her hand. Mom inquired, what was wrong with her hand. Lauren said she had been climbing a tree. Mom asked if she reached the top, and when Lauren said she did, Mom said with great enthusiasm, "That's the way to go!" She asked Caitlin where she was living and was happy to hear Caitlin say Boston (just for a visit), though she also seemed enthusiastic to hear of the other places Caitlin had traveled to. As she had done numerous times in the past, she gave her last measure of strength to encourage them. They still feel her spirit strongly inside them. I am very happy my daughters were able to get to know my mother over the last three decades.

That evening an assessment nurse from Gilcrest Hospice came over. She was very reassuring. She saw that we were providing comfort and care and understood we were following my mother's wish not to take any extraordinary measures.

That night I pulled a mattress into Mom's room so I could sleep beside her. I didn't want her to journey into that night alone while she journeyed into the nighttime of her life. I thought often that night of one of her favorite Dylan Thomas poems, "Do Not Go Gentle Into That Good Night."

She awoke several times during the night. Just as I had done with our children when they were babies, I awoke with her. Once she sat straight up in bed, and then turned and looked at me with great apprehension. And then smiled when she saw me and said, "Oh you are there." Then she calmly lay down again. Other times I would soothe her and sing to her as I had done for Caity and Lauren when they were babies.

During my mother's last day on this earth, she slipped into a coma, breathing very heavily and rapidly. Tish spent time with her; I suggested she read to Mom from the children's book that my mother had written, *The Butterfly and the Stone*. I had heard that people in a coma could still hear. Tish later told me she had to stop reading when she got to the passage about the butterfly flying off. It was just too close to my mother's departure. That evening we listened to classical music with her as she drew her final breath and then was still.

Clearly, it was hard to let go. I was reminded of this when I was spooning her ashes into the lovely blue urn my daughter Lauren had made. I only wanted to put a small fraction of the ashes into the urn. Lauren pointed out, "You seem to be having trouble saying goodbye to your mother." Indeed, that was and is still true...

Though I still wished she had stayed a little longer, I wished her no further pain. I miss hearing her wonderful (though at times infuriating) voice and miss hearing her full and vital laughter. No longer will I hear her call out my name to put away the groceries, to get the mail, to fire Jay, to know I was there. Yet, I can still hear her call within.

PART II

Recovery of Your Life through Empowerment

Relationships are critical. Hope, trust, understanding, connecting deeply, and believing in another person are crucial to recovery of life. This is a way of relating that was frequently absent in my interactions of my past. It is relating from a place deep inside the heart. This is how we are with a really good friend or lover. You feel you are on the same wavelength. There is chemistry, you resonate. Most of us can recall such moments. Can you recall your first "love affair," the one with your mother when you were an infant? Or perhaps the re-creation of those moments when you took care of your own infant? When I gaze into the eyes of my children, my spouse, a friend, or other family members, I feel their world. I can experience their feelings of themselves and of me. I become gradually more conscious through those relationships. These are *mutually loving* relationships.

The philosopher Martin Buber eloquently captured the importance of "deep relatedness" in his book *I and Thou*. He contrasted I-Thou relationships with I-It contacts. According to Buber, I-It contacts are not relationships. They occur between people and machines or people who see each other as objects. During the first two decades of my life, my world had become increasingly a world of I-It contacts (including my contact with myself). My recovery involved shifting from I-It

77

contacts to I-Thou relationships. I have had to feel secure in the I-Thou inner relationship with myself to proceed with this book.

Many years ago, when first attempting to write this book I was afraid that in the process of telling my story, my new Self would take over and get rid of my older self. My older self was afraid of my newer Self. This fear of my newer Self could have kept me (and others labeled with schizophrenia) trapped in the past. Instead, I said to that older part of myself, "You are a part of me and at the moment I put down each word, I am part of you." This is almost the same magical transformation of ourselves that happens when we truly engage with another person. **Something about being in deep relationships allows the variety of my seemingly independent selves to come together into a community of selves that I call my Self.**

Two decades ago, I wrote about it this way:

There is inside of me a Self, a spirit which is gradually becoming more aware of others and me. That Self is becoming my guide. It encompasses all that I am. My Self includes — but is greater than — my chemicals, my background, and my traumas. It is the me I am seeking to become in my relationships at that moment of creative uncertainty when I make contact with another. In that moment when we together defy the odds and say 'yes', our lives will go on regardless of how we live the following moment. We are all inventing our lives at each moment.

I now add to this:

We indeed need deep connection with each other and our Self to be able to invent our lives at each moment. These relationships form a bridge to the next moment and allow us to live in the uncertainty needed to allow something new and unexpected to emerge from our deepest Self. In the absence of such relationships we are condemned to forever rework the same thoughts and ideas, causing them and the trapped thinker to separate from the reality of the times.

Another philosopher whose writing resonates with me is the Russian philosopher and literary critic, Mikhail Bakhtin. He carried on the tradition of Buber, further elaborating the essence of dialogue. He stated,

"Dialogue is life. To live is to be in dialogue. To be in dialogue is to be human." This is why I believe that recovery of our humanity is best achieved through establishing an I-Thou dialogue. I-Thou relationships are most alive in the present moment. They are diminished by focusing on the past or the future at the expense of the present. Excessive focus on the past or the future may lead to psychosis. Open Dialogue may be successful because it brings the person and their network back to the present moment together.

There have been places and periods in United States history when mental health recovery rates were high. In 1987, Courtney Harding released the results of a study tracking 269 patients with schizophrenia and other psychotic disorders who were discharged from Vermont State Hospital between 1955–1960. Her study showed that 68% of these patients demonstrated complete or very significant recovery. When she compared the rate of recovery in Maine during the same period, the result was 49%. She concluded that a vital difference between the recovery rates in the two states was that in Vermont there had been an expectation that people would recover and that programming was based around this premise. In contrast, there was a much lower expectation for recovery in Maine, with the primary treatment focus placed on maintenance.

FOUR

Lessons I Learned
During Recovery of My Life

In the decades since my three psychiatric hospitalizations, I have asked myself, "What happened to me? Why did it happen? How can I prevent it from happening again?" I have realized that deep inside there was a *me* yearning to emerge. As a young man I blocked my emergence. I was merely intent on making a great discovery in the lab. All other aspects of life seemed secondary.

Now I realize I was strangling my life and spontaneity. My rationality and ambition were poisoning my relationships and depriving my inner Self of growing. My inner Self was starving. That deeper me refused to go along with this approach and rebelled. I sought out ways to experience the world directly instead of reading about it. I only knew I was missing fulfillment. I tried modern dance, different kinds of therapy, many relationships, and drugs. This headlong assault on my rationality brought on my breakdowns as I searched for breakthroughs. Slowly, I started to learn about this deeper me through therapy, friends, and journaling. I learned that what I most yearned for was genuine human connection at a deep level. In fact, **I now believe that connecting is the primary and essential ingredient of self-growth, and thereby, recovery of life**. Evoking the growth of one's deeper Self through vital relationships is the essence of love. A dear friend sent me a meditation by Louis Évely that captures this process:

Loving people means summoning them forth
    with the loudest and most insistent of calls:
it means stirring up in them
    a mute and hidden being
        who can't help leaping at the sound of our voice —
a being so new
        that even those who carried him
            didn't know him,
        and yet so authentic
            that they can't fail to recognize him
once they discover him . . .
    To love someone is to bid them to live,
            invite them to grow.
Since people don't have the courage to mature
        unless someone has faith in them,
    we have to reach those we meet
        at the level they stopped developing,
            where they were given up as hopeless,
            and so withdrew into
                    themselves
                and began to secrete
                    a protective shell
            because they thought they were alone
                    and no one cared.
    They have to feel they are loved very deeply
                and very boldly
    before they dare to feel humble and kind,
            affectionate, sincere
                and vulnerable.

This book is about the theme raised in this lovely meditation; it is about the importance of love and friendship. I came to these conclusions long after I had recovered. I recovered through finding love and friendship but it has taken me years to reconstruct how I did so. The sentiment of this beautiful piece resonates deeply within me — I feel a special bond with the author. Each of us carries within us a mute being waiting to leap forth at the sound of our lover's and friends' voices. We can only come to know that inner being through another person who summons forth that being by their caring, understanding, and love. We nourish the emergence of that inner being by connecting with people who bring out that side of us and by learning to be with ourselves in such a loving manner. If we do not nourish our inner being, it will find other ways to feed itself and make itself known.

As my mute being emerged, I realized that it was the deeper me. I realized that by experiencing the mute being, I was really experiencing my deeper Self. At first it was hard to live in such intensity. In fact, my first real experience with that mute being inside me was during my periods of silence, which came with each intense emotional state called "psychosis." I think I *became* that mute being during those times. The mute being inside me took charge of my superficial, rigid self. I found that my mute being would only relinquish that control when I acknowledged that it had as much right to participate in my life as my usual, day-to-day speaking self. In time, I came to understand and appreciate the reality that only by valuing every moment could I be both the feeling, mute being and the rational, speaking being. I now understand that the emergence of the formerly mute me that had been here all along changes how I see myself and the world around me. I feel the emergence of my mute being has reversed the flow of my experiencing the world. Before these breakthroughs, I would always stand back and plan and reflect before I would act. I was in a state of *heartless mind*, to use a Buddhist description. Then I tried pure action, or *mindless heart*. Neither was satisfying. Now I feel and think at the same time, in the present moment. We might call this state of being "heartful mindfulness." I think this has been possible because my moments last longer. I feel more in control of myself and feel I can relate in a more genuine fashion. Thinking and feeling together gives greater life to all that I do.

I believe that repeating an important story in slightly different variations is a vital way to deepen understanding. Recently, I caught a glimpse of this phenomenon in a dream. *In the dream, I kept going back to a difficult path I sensed I could not traverse. The path seemed to disappear into the ocean. There was a steep cliff beside me. It seemed there was no way to progress to a place that I wanted to reach further down the coast. The seasons changed and the water receded enough to reveal a little more of the path. I retraced my steps. I stopped a passerby to ask if there was another route, and he pointed to slightly higher ground. I could see another route.* I awoke feeling relieved that I could find my way, and also felt the importance of repeatedly approaching the same problem from slightly different angles. I also saw the importance of getting opinions from others rather than just relying upon myself.

At the heart of my recovery is the recovery of my humanity through self-transformation and relationships of "authentic dialogue," as will be discussed more in what follows. My lived experience of recovering my humanity has played a pivotal role in my work to help others. I was asked several years ago how my personal journey led to my decision to become a psychiatrist. Here was my reply:

> *My personal journey is a very significant part of my reason for becoming a psychiatrist — wanting to bring to the field what I wish had been there when I was going through my psychoses. I very clearly remember thinking during my second hospitalization, "If the people who are talking to me had only been where I am right now, they'd know the way to communicate with me so that I would feel once again part of the world around me." I also hoped there'd be a way to be helped short of having to be involuntarily hospitalized, which I went through three times.*

Relationships of authentic dialogue nurture a person's recovery of humanity. Recovery is one of the consumer/survivor movement's unique contributions to the transformation of our system, our society, and our lives. Recovery is very personal and requires both a personal change and changes in relationships. **From a recovery perspective, emotional distress is an opportunity for growth, through self-transformation aided by loving, hopeful relationships that enable a person to build a full, playful, and gratifying life in the community of their choice.**

Recovery does not merely mean a return to where a person was before any life-changing experiences. Recovery means much more than that. In Spanish, the word recovery is literally *recuperación*, which is closer to the English word "recuperation." But in our consumer/survivor movement, recovery means much more than recuperation, which suggests recovery from a cold or a broken arm. We do not see recovery as such a narrow medical term, nor is recovery the same thing as a cure. For consumer/survivors, recovery is better translated as *recobrar la vida* or "recover your life." I recovered my life through finding my authentic Voice, which enabled me to fully live my life as an active member of the community.

The word "recovery" was at the core of the President's New Freedom Commission on Mental Health report of 2003, whose vision statement is: "We see a future when everyone with mental illness will recover." I was the only person serving on the New Freedom Commission with lived experience of having recovered from an extreme mental health condition. I insisted that there be a vision of recovery to unify our recommendations. The New Freedom Commission's vision has inspired consumer/survivors and advocates worldwide to create a culture that fosters the recovery of our humanity through individual and collective growth. We added "our" to the phrase "recovery of humanity" in order to emphasize the mutuality of growth and transformation. We need to get beyond a world that segregates the sick and the well, the provider and the consumer. In its place, we propose a world of equality of power, respect, and dignity. After all, the diminishing of anyone's humanity diminishes mine.

Recovery has been impeded by the thinking of a majority of providers who continue to embrace a narrow definition of the conditions from which people are recovering. Presently, most practitioners and the general public are still taught that severe psychological problems are primarily due to a chemical imbalance. The problems are labeled forms of mental illness, of which the most severe is considered to be schizophrenia.

I have given hundreds of talks describing my recovery from schizophrenia and am often told by professionals that I must have been misdiagnosed because they know that people with "true schizophrenia" do not recover. Many people in our movement who tell of their recovery are similarly dismissed. This dilemma reached its greatest extreme recently. A friend of mine was taking a graduate course in psychopathology. The professor gravely told the class that people with schizophrenia never recover. My friend exclaimed, "I have a friend who had been diagnosed with schizophrenia and recovered." With great assurance the professor replied, "Well, he must have been misdiagnosed." My friend called and asked if I really had had schizophrenia. (Notably she avoided using the dehumanizing phrase, "had been a schizophrenic.")

I had been diagnosed according to the DSM II (Diagnostic and Statistical Manual), the official reference for mental health diagnoses at any given time. The DSM II dates from 1968. Since this question had been raised before, we decided to see if I would have fit the criteria for schizophrenia according to the more recent DSM IV. We found that my second episode of psychosis fit the DSM IV criteria for schizophrenia:

- *I was unable to work, socialize, or carry out activities of daily living in an accepted manner for more than six months.*
- *I was paranoid and experienced catatonia for nearly a month.*
- *I had ideas of reference (I thought the TV was talking to me), I heard voices, and I thought my nurse was actually my sister's friend who had been killed years before.*

When my friend presented our evidence to the professor, he looked gravely concerned and said, "Now we have a case of a disabled psychiatrist." This response showed how the belief that people cannot recover is deeply ingrained in our collective psyche. Even evidence to the contrary cannot shake that belief. This inability to accept evidence contrary to existing theories is an illustration of one of the ways psychiatry is not an evidence-based practice. It is impossible to have true evidence-based psychiatry as long as the beliefs of the field are not based on the evidence that people recover from extreme mental health conditions. That is why one of the sayings of our movement is, "We are the evidence that people recover." Instead, it is more accurate to call mainstream psychiatry a faith-based practice. Indeed, psychiatrist Robert Coles and many others have concluded that present-day psychiatry is closer to a religion than a science.

I have been asked on several occasions to give people a certificate of recovery. So I and a team at NEC developed a list of seven characteristics of a person who has fully recovered from a severe mental health condition. A person who has recovered:

- *Makes their own decisions in collaboration with other supportive people outside the mental health system*

- *Has a meaningful and fulfilling network of friends outside the mental health professionals*
- *Has achieved a major social role and identity other than consumer (such as student, parent, worker)*
- *Uses medication as one tool among many freely chosen by the individual to assist in their day-to-day life (used as the chronically normal persons use medication)*
- *Is capable of expressing and understanding emotions to such a degree that the person can cope with severe emotional distress without it interrupting their social role and without them being labeled symptoms*
- *Has a Global Assessment of Functioning Scale score of greater than sixty-one, which means they are: "functioning pretty well, some meaningful interpersonal relationships and 'most untrained people would not consider him sick'"*
- *Has a sense of Self defined by oneself through life experience and interaction with peers*

Another way to recover is to reject the whole idea that there are mental health conditions. There are people in our movement who adopt this point of view and I admire them. I just think we need an avenue out of the mental health trap for those persons and their families who are presently deeply ensnared.

From my more than forty years of lived experience of recovery, clinical practice, and working as an advocate, I have discovered numerous recovery lessons. In addition, Patricia Deegan and I carried out qualitative recovery research. From those studies and experience in the field, I have come up with the following set of recovery values.

Recovery Values

Recovery Often Begins With Deep Distress Called "Symptoms"

At first, I thought that my journeys into other realities were the symptoms of an illness: schizophrenia. It took awhile for me to realize that this concept of mental health issues turned the truth on its head. In fact, I now see that my journeys to other realities were necessary to my personal growth and recovery. I understand that emotional distress can offer clues revealing how to grow beyond blockages — rather than as merely symptoms of a disease.

I first grasped this idea during an interview with Sally Zinman, a founder of our consumer/survivor movement. I asked her, as I have asked many others, "When did your recovery begin?" She told me her recovery began when she first had what others described as symptoms of mental illness. Her particular symptom was that she became convinced she was not Sally Zinman and her parents were not really her parents. Her conviction caused her parents to declare her delusional, and she was locked in a private residential program for two years. This period included several months confinement in a basement, clad only in her underwear. Gradually she realized that to regain her freedom she had to comply with society's description of who she was. She was released after two years but her actual recovery began with her conviction that she was someone other than the person everyone else thought she was. She learned to continue that journey to self-discovery through finding new work and new relationships that reinforced her new identity as a social reformer.

In 1973, a Jungian psychiatrist, John Weir Perry, stated that unusual thoughts and behaviors, which many in the medical community define as signs and symptoms of mental illness, are, in fact, signs of health. Dr. Perry viewed psychosis as efforts by a person's deepest psyche to reintegrate in a more harmonious fashion. Dr. Perry stated that if there was an illness, it preceded the psychosis. The psychosis was an extreme emotional state by which the person attempts to go beyond the interference with an integrated sense of Self due to trauma and loss. In addition, the pioneering Austrian psychotherapist Alfred Adler once noted that what we call symptoms are really attempts to solve inner problems.

My early life as a mockingbird was a period of stunted emotional growth. I was cautious, I numbed my feelings, and I was closed to new experiences and relationships. When my first wife departed, I was awakened to the reality that I was not really living my own life. I was living for other people. So I flooded myself with new experiences of my own choice: dance, art, therapy, politics, love, and consciousness-expanding drugs. I opened many previously locked doors, entered musty rooms, and exposed darkened windows to the sunlight and space I had been afraid to experience. While I was going through this multiplicity of new experiences in the evenings, I was still working at NIMH during the day, attempting to discover answers according to a narrow chemical explanation for emotions, dreams, and memories. It was very difficult to accept that my bench science was too narrow for the person I wanted to be, and what my world was becoming. Only when I took mescaline did this realization come through in great clarity. Even then, it first appeared as the waking dreams called delusions by the conventional world. My conviction that everyone in the world was a robot was a crystallization of the mechanistic, robotic life I had been living for the previous twenty-four years. I wish it had not taken six years for me to concede that this mechanized life was not for me. It seemed I had to go through many processes in therapy and life to come to that realization.

While I was living in Dupont Circle, Washington, D.C., I was in an area of cultural, social, and political upheaval with opportunities for creative change. My personal evolution was greatly aided by the times, during which many of the older social traditions came under collective questioning. I witnessed the emergence of movements advocating for the civil rights of people of color, women, gays, and for persons labeled with mental illness.

Authentic Relationships are Crucial to Recovery of Our Humanity

How do we engage our Self in life-affirming spirals? Relationships of care, support, and love are primary. Though I started to build my own understanding by working from my personal experience of recovery from schizophrenia, I want to affirm some very old wisdom from John Donne: "No one is an island." What affects one of us affects all of us. My recovery from schizophrenia has been a recovery of my humanity. And yet I can only experience my humanity when the world around me also experiences its humanity. First and foremost, recovery is recovery of our shared humanity. Conversely, what is described as mental illness is humanity lost.

We lose our humanity when we traumatize, frighten, and isolate each other. In fact, the most fundamental aspect of trauma is any event that interferes with a person's capacity to experience their humanity. This happens when we disrespect each other. This happens when we view human differences as imperfections that should be surgically corrected. This happens when we discriminate and disregard others' basic human rights to life, liberty, and equality.

Recently, a consumer I have worked with for many years came to my office in great distress. He had made steady progress getting in touch with his feelings but was convinced he was getting sick again. As he paced the floor saying he couldn't stay, he kept avoiding looking at me. I looked at him directly, attempting to get his attention. I said, with a conviction based on experience, that he was capable of facing the feelings he was experiencing. He looked surprised, but intrigued. "But I have never had these feelings before," he complained. "I must need a new medication." I reassured him that his medication was at a proper level. I told him that a peer of his, whom he respected, recently described the role of medication as forming the foundation, while he worked to construct the house of his recovery. I suggested that he had to make an active effort to build a deeper understanding of himself. I told him he was just starting to feel the anxiety that everyone feels as a part of living. He calmed down and became curious, engaging in direct conversation. I told him I had confidence in his ability to continue with his recovery. His confidence was building and he stayed with the visit. He just needed reminding that what he was experiencing was not a part of his illness, but actually part of his recovery. If I had colluded with his denial of feelings by saying the problem was chemical and he just needed more or a different medication, he would not have experienced this element of his innate humanity. In fact, I would have just reinforced his conviction that he was basically a chemical machine and not a human being.

Over the years, I have tried to remember that during my periods of distress I felt best when people talked to me as they would to a person who was not labeled mentally ill, when they treated me as a full human being — even though I did not appear to be fully with them. I think this attitude and approach is incredibly important in overcoming stigma and discrimination. On a deeper level it helps overcome the sense of being discredited and devalued that is embedded in the label of "mental illness."

The fundamental problem with our mental health system is that labeling a person with mental illness consolidates a marginalization of those who have already been traumatized and rejected. It segregates anyone so labeled from the rest of humanity, as well as from their own humanity. The basic human rights as conferred by the U.S. Constitution are, in fact, taken from us. We literally lose citizenship. Recovery means the restoration of citizenship in a sense far beyond the legal framework of citizenship. Michael Rowe, Co-Director of the Yale Program for Recovery and Community Health, views recovery through a citizenship framework. He believes that recovery involves not only the work of an individual with a professional, but also of that person in relation to their community.

I believe that the lessons that others and I have learned through our recovery from severe emotional states can kindle the spark of hope and purpose in the hearts of those trying to make a life in the world. Though these ideas were forged from the hot steel of recovery from "mental illness," they reverberate across this country and around the world. This is because we are all connected through our human experiences and human needs. A friend in Japan said it well when he bade farewell to me at a train station in Tokyo, "I resonate with you."

When I can live my real life through expressing my authentic Voice, I am strong, courageous, and loving. Life then has meaning because it is my life and I am proud of it. I can feel the meaning as a stronger pulse to my heart and veins. As Dylan Thomas wrote, "The force that through the green fuse drives the flower, Drives my green age." This force of life is the revitalization we seek to bring about through Emotional CPR.

During most of my early life, I lived for others. It was like living a false life, with a falsetto voice. My voice only came from my throat, not from my chest, because it did not resonate with the person I truly was. The last vestige of my false self fell away recently at a presentation in Santa Barbara. At first it seemed like a routine presentation to a group of emerging recovery leaders. It was, however, a new workshop I had been creating called "Finding Our Voice" (see Chapter Seven). As I stepped into the middle of the circle I noticed a new feeling of inner unity and peace as I spoke. My words came from my deepest conviction. As I sensed the group's affirmation, I felt an emotional clarity,

91

that I had not experienced before. My words resonated with my being and I truly felt I was finding my Voice. I could see in each person's face a glow of recognition. I felt I was truly reaching a deep part of their being. I felt I was reaching a part of their being which had been sleeping but was eager to play an active role in their life. I felt I could see them coming alive. In their coming to life, I was also coming to life at a deeper level. This dance of recognition, of mutual affirmation, seems to be at the heart of the emotional dialogue, which I believe fosters recovery and development of our deeper Self. In Chapter Nine, I will discuss ways of improving emotional dialogue through eCPR.

The importance of being authentic was brought home again at another event. I gave a talk in Los Angeles at a fundraiser for a friend who was starting a nonprofit to spread the message of recovery. A woman asked what element played the most important factor in my recovery. I cited my therapist, Dr. Semchyshyn. I emphasized that I wanted him to be "real." Later in the event, Dr. Dan Dorman suggested we should give a presentation on the theme, "Why being real works." During the discussion Dr. Dorman explained that when a person who provides help is authentic and real, the person in distress's real Self emerges. He should know. He spent three years assisting a woman to emerge from a catatonic psychosis through therapy, without medication, as described in his book *Dante's Cure*.

Learning What Deeper Reality Is

Since being crazy is being out of touch with reality, I love to ask audiences, "What is reality?" The cleverest answer was, "Reality is a collective hunch." But I think that there is a deeper reality, that is appreciated by our deepest Self. This is the level of reality most essential to our existence. It is the level that being real can reach. Perhaps we could call this our real Self; the one we need to nourish or else we die. Even more than being nourished, this real Self may need to go through rebirths.

When I meditate, I feel closer to my real Self. My real Self is the source of my authentic Voice. Paradoxically, I can only connect deeply with others and lose myself in that experience when I can feel and express my real Self. In doing so, my real Self resonates with the reality of others' Selves. As with the African concept of *ubuntu*, I can only experience my deeper humanity through connecting with others at the level of their humanity. I think we have a hunger to feed our real Self. When we do not attend to that need, we shrivel inside. We know when this is happening and nothing else is as important as meeting that deep need to nourish our real Self. In my own situation, spoken words lost all meaning. Words seemed to interfere with this deeper need. So I stopped talking. I felt I would only talk again if there were a good reason. But first I needed verification that my existence mattered to someone. I had to first check out the sincerity and authenticity of that person through my heart. Then my thoughts and words would follow. A vivid illustration of this yearning for authentic dialogue came in my contact with the corpsman in the emergency room of Bethesda Naval Hospital. I now believe that what is labeled psychosis is not due to a deficit in thinking but to an intense concentration on the most essential questions of life. Day-to-day necessities seem minor in comparision to the deeper questions such as "Who am I?" "Why am I here on this earth?" "What will give meaning and purpose to my life?"

Hope Is an Essential Aspect of Recovery

Emotional traumas sever our sense of existing throughout the course of a durable past, present, and future. Instead, existence seems to be only a series of fleeting moments, which can easily be blown away. This leaves us hopeless. Sometimes we need to borrow hope and absorb a sense of existing from someone else. It seems like we carry a bucket for hope with us. When our hope bucket is nearly empty, then we need to fill it up from someone whose bucket is full.

The idea of a bucket of hope came from a question asked by a woman, in a peer support group, whose husband had recently committed suicide. She asked, "What do you do when you try as hard as you can to give hope to someone but it isn't enough?" I shared the story of the nurse in Japan who said she wanted to absorb as much hope in her heart as possible from me so she could share that hope when she returned to teaching her nursing students. I had an image of her heart as her hope bucket. That image appeared to have some power because later one of the other group participants said she wanted to give people buckets into which they could put reminders of everything that made them hopeful. It is through the establishment of authentic relationships that a person is able to borrow the hope of having a future. In this context, it is tragic that many well-meaning mental health workers paint such a bleak future, when exactly the opposite is what is sorely needed. The bleakness can lead to suicide. After all, hopelessness is the greatest risk factor for suicide. I fear that the increase in the rate of suicide in the industrial world among persons experiencing psychosis is because the mental health providers are robbing us of hope. Recently, the mother of a twenty-eight-year-old woman came to see me. She was in great distress because her daughter had just been diagnosed with schizophrenia at a renowned teaching hospital. She and her daughter were told that the young woman would never get a job, never marry, and never drive. I helped restore some hope by telling of my own recovery.

The importance of hope is also illustrated by the story of a young boy who attended a talk I gave about my own recovery. At lunchtime, I met his mother. She said that I might have saved his life. She told me that when he was ten he was told he had bipolar disorder and that he would never recover. As a result of the finality of that diagnosis, he became suicidal and had remained so until he heard my talk. When he heard me describe my own recovery, and that recovery occurs for many others, he was no longer suicidal for the first time in three years.

We See Through Our Heart that Love Is the True Reality

I am sharing my journey from fear to anger to love. It is a story of freeing myself and allowing others to free me from fear and darkness. From the heart of darkness, I have traveled to light-heartedness. The image below of two hearts speaks to me. It was painted by a person going through recovery in Denmark. When I was young, I hardened my heart to the world. I said I would not allow anyone too close. That would be too risky. I didn't want to be hurt again as I had been when I was traumatized by my teacher. I felt the same way about all aspects of my environment. I didn't want to listen or look too closely at people. People frightened me. I concentrated on books and science. Those were safe areas. They were areas I felt secure in. They were areas I felt I could control. I had the blackened heart.

This left me separated from others and from myself. I felt I could not reach other people, which left me empty-hearted. I tried love once in high school. I gave my heart to a girl whole-heartedly. But she

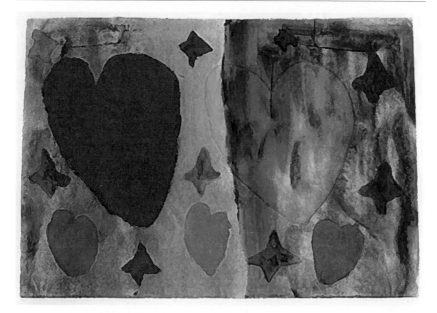

dropped me and I was broken hearted. I cried so uncontrollably that she was very concerned.

After that, I became cold-hearted and held my feelings in. I kept my body very rigid and stuck to a rigid routine in my science. I wanted to explain the world by molecules. It was a static world, where all the answers were to be discovered outside of me. I did not feel I had any *me* inside.

But my spirit would not stand for this loveless state any longer. I first glimpsed another world on mescaline when I felt connected through my feet to all the other persons on this globe. I have not looked back since. My heart opened and I love humanity. I want to make the world a more loving place where people can grow and care and believe in each other. As the fox said in Antoine de Saint-Exupéry's *The Little Prince*, we see truth through our hearts not through our eyes. *"Voici mon secret. Il est très simple: on ne voit bien qu'avec le cœur. L'essentiel est invisible pour les yeux."* (Here is my secret. It is very simple: It is only with the heart that one can truly see; what is essential is invisible to the eye.)

This same essential truth is found in Margery Williams' children's classic, *The Velveteen Rabbit:* you only become your authentic Self or

Real when you are loved. The Rabbit asks the Skin Horse how a stuffed animal becomes Real:

> *"It doesn't happen all at once," said the Skin Horse. "You become. It takes a long time. That's why it doesn't happen often to people who break easily, or have sharp edges, or who have to be carefully kept. Generally, by the time you are Real, most of your hair has been loved off, and your eyes drop out and you get loose in your joints and very shabby. But these things don't matter at all, because once you are Real you can't be ugly, except to people who don't understand."*

During my first twenty-four years, I only connected at the superficial level. This kept me at a safe distance from my feelings, and a safe distance from all others, which in turn left me feeling very lonely. This distance also kept me frightened. Then I broke down, which I had to do to break through the shell I had built around me for protection. I broke through the barriers I had erected to keep people at a distance.

Now I seek out deeper relationships. I seek the experience of love, for only through love can I become the person I dream of being. Only through love can I truly be born and be the spontaneous being that has lain mutely below the surface of my consciousness.

We carry each other in our hearts. Several years ago I stopped at my mother's local 24-hour store to buy butter pecan ice cream, her favorite. The woman at the store lit up when I said it was for my ninety-four-year-old mother.

"How is she?" she inquired. "I was worried about her."

I could clearly hear and see her concern. Her response warmed my heart, and as I walked out, I thought of how the heart of a community is in the hearts of each of its members. When we each care it helps us all a great deal.

Another illuminating moment came when I was discussing recovery with a group of consumers at a statewide consumer conference in Louisiana. They agreed that being an authentic person was essential. They also agreed when I quoted the man in Japan who said that for him recovery meant "becoming in touch with his true Self."

Then a young man who had been quiet much of the morning asked, "How do you know when you are experiencing your true Self?"

This question riveted me as well as the rest of the group. One woman said that when she reads something that makes sense to her, she knows she is closer to her Self. Someone else said it is in the response of other people; they often can see our true Self before we do. Another said it comes from following your dreams. Afterward, the young man shared with me that he had been diagnosed with schizophrenia, and he wondered if he would ever recover. I tried to share some of my hope with him from my bucket of hope. His eyes shone a little brighter when I said, "Hope for recovery starts by asking the question you asked earlier."

Sally Zinman, whom I mentioned before, is a dramatic example of someone who was not able to nourish her inner being. She stated that her recovery began when she refused to be the person she had been told she was. Her story suggests that her recovery required that she throw off the image that her parents had fashioned for her. She then had to create a new Sally. She went through her identity quest when she was thirty-two years old, instead of during adolescence, which may explain why she had to go about it so drastically. She had to vigorously throw off her superimposed false self. This jettisoning of a false self, created by parents and other authorities, is very much like the description of a divided self famously described by R.D. Laing.

A similar process is depicted in the journey of the main character in the 2006 movie, *Stranger than Fiction*. Love plays a major role in the emergence of his inner being. Once that inner being emerges, its existence literally saves his life. Screenwriter Zach Helm allowed the main character to realize that the little acts of kindness towards others are more important than anything else. Another movie with a similar theme is *Reign Over Me*. In this 2007 film, the protagonist suffers from PTSD (Post-traumatic Stress Disorder) of such severity that he is living in his own reality and has given up on work. However, due to a random meeting with a friend from college he begins the process of healing. The Academy Award-winning film *The Soloist* shows that a crucial element in the recovery process is a caring, loving relationship with one person reaching out toward another whose life has turned inward.

Finding People Who Believe In You
Helps You Believe In Yourself

One person can have a surprising impact by assisting someone who is feeling stuck and hopeless to open up to new possibilities and horizons. A number of people in a recovery group shared their thoughts about the power of this effect on them. Many confessed their surprise when they encountered this effect personally.

My wife has had that effect on me. She has always believed that I could do many things, even before I thought I could. On the first day of my residency in psychiatry, she offered to walk with me the five blocks to the hospital where my training began. I bravely told her that I didn't need her help, even though I was in a state close to terror. Luckily she insisted, and she greatly boosted my confidence on that threatening day.

I remember a friend in Washington who helped me in this manner around the time of my move from D.C. to Boston for my residency. I was reluctant to leave Washington; it had been my home for eight years. But I also wanted to get my training at Cambridge Hospital. Then my friend simply suggested that I think of my move to Boston as an adventure. It freed me to look at the excitement ahead instead of the loss of past connections and history. His words helped, but it was also the attitude with which he said it. It was clear that he believed I could do it — he believed in me. (I also had great admiration for him because he was losing the use of his legs from a progressive neurological condition but still continued to work on improving his life.)

In our qualitative study of recovery at NEC, a majority of the thirty people interviewed cited the vital importance of being with "a person who believed in me" as essential to their recovery process. To convey this attitude, a person assisting someone in recovery needs to use a form of direct, open, and spontaneous communication. (Something, alas, that seems to be trained out of many professionals.) Nearly every consumer concurs that they received their best help from the least clinically trained staff in hospitals. Independently, they all noted there was at least one person like this. Often it was a residential or rehabilitation facilitator who was able to communicate this level of belief and reach the deepest part of the person in need. One subject said he could detect "belief signals" from the people who understood him. These were people who believed in his capacity to get a life, to take responsibility, and to change.

I think having someone believe in a person in distress's potential to recover is an essential factor in helping free people from being trapped in monologue. Perhaps an important factor in getting trapped in monologue is becoming convinced that one does not have a future and that one does not have the potential to grow and to live a fuller life. This dead end feeling can cause one's spirit and self to curl inward, in a spiral of death. As Bob Dylan sang, "Whoever isn't busy being born is busy dying."

My therapist was a good example of a person who believed in me. He always found meaning in my seemingly disconnected thoughts. He gave me credit for insights that seemed to come from him. For instance, one day he said he saw me now devoting more energy to filling in the lateral parts of my life, such as fun and recreation, instead of putting all the emphasis on the vertical components, such as competing to be the very best at work and school. I said to Dr. Semchyshyn that this seemed a good insight, and he sincerely said that it came from me, not from him. He said his role was to reflect back to me my own insights so that I could hear them in a new way. So, in addition to believing in my capacity to come up with the ideas needed to free me, he was able to condense my own musings into a form that I could understand more clearly. In doing so, he helped me with self-understanding.

Pick a Line of Work That You Love and That Fulfills You

My recovery was also assisted by my work as a peer coach to people in acute emotional distress at a free clinic. As I helped them through their distress, I came to understand more about myself. When diagnosed, a person often feels as if their ability to make a contribution is negated. However, it is through the very act of sharing ourselves that we feel valuable and still connected to the human race.

There are a number of other ways that my own experience has helped me reach very distressed individuals. I have always believed that there is a core of strength hiding inside each person, no matter how deeply upset they are. The trick is to always remember the power residing within, and to be *with* the person in a manner that conveys confidence. Then they can draw upon that hidden strength within themselves. In order to facilitate confidence and instill a sense of hope within someone in need, the person offering help needs to be authentic. This is later described in greater detail in the section devoted to eCPR.

For the past three decades, I have provided psychiatric care to countless mental health consumers in hospitals and clinics. During this same period, I have also been part of the consumer movement. Observing and living the opposing sides within the system has been a source of some tension. Yet for all the conflicting emotions, this has also been personally rewarding. By working intensely with providers, families, and consumers, I have learned to bridge these worlds, acting as a translator or ambassador to each side. I have found that the common ground is recovery. It is an ideal that consumers, families, and providers can all agree upon. This agreement is a new development. To reach this common ground, providers have had to stop being convinced that remission was the best anyone could hope for. Families have needed to understand the importance of their children gaining greater autonomy. Consumer/survivor leaders have had to accept that there are times when persons in severe distress need clinical assistance.

Through my work on the New Freedom Commission for Mental Health, I was able to bring these three worlds together by getting the groups to agree on a common vision of recovery. That vision gives hope to millions of consumer/survivors and their families. We established the major goal of transforming the mental health system from a maintenance, symptom-reduction system to a consumer- and family-driven, recovery-oriented approach to care. The commission recommended that consumers and families fully participate in training, policy development, service evaluation, and service delivery. That report feeds the dreams of consumers and families across this country and around the world. In addition, I worked with the commission to recommend greatly reducing the use of seclusion and restraint. I was asked numerous times how I had been able to make such a significant impact when I was the only consumer/survivor on the commission. These questions inspired me to create a training program for advocates called "Finding our Voice."

Helping Others Helps Yourself

"Through helping others we help ourself" is a principle of peer work. It is also the twelfth step of Alcoholics Anonymous. In the mental health field, this principle is manifest by the many who want to give back what they received, or want to supply what they did not receive. For me, my wish to become a psychiatrist arose from both of these motivations.

I believe that the challenge of reaching persons whose own distress has driven them deep inside draws us further towards our own humanity. This may be because we can only reach another person in distress when we are able to be deeply in tune with our deepest Self.

From our traumas, we each grow a thick, protective shell. My sister loved her turtles. She felt a bond and empathy with them. She, like them, grew a protective shell to protect her from the world. I wish I could reach her. I, too, grew a shell, but fortunately broke through with the help of a loving therapist, friends, and family. The essential aspect of reaching a person in their shell is to believe in the person they can become, even when they no longer believe it is possible that they can become that person. The most important expression of that belief is the spontaneous expression of oneself to the other person. When I was in greatest distress, only the most authentic expressions of the essential inner Self from another person could reach me. These expressions were often nonverbal and emotional. They were the most human of expressions. Rick, the corpsman, actually saw the *me* inside that I was afraid to experience and express. He peered inside with his heart. With his heart he saw that I was still there, and I in turn, was able to see him with my heart. When I was in my most withdrawn state, I refused so insistently to talk that I was no longer able to talk even when I wanted to. I told myself, "I will only come out when the world of people around me is safe. I will only come out when I can truly trust the people around me." I was testing the people around me to see if they really cared.

Trusting Oneself and Others

Noted psychologist Eric Erikson asserted in *Childhood and Society* that trusting oneself and others is the fundamental first aspect in any major developmental step in life. Erikson called this type of trust "basic trust," because of the need to have it established at one's deepest level. During periods of severe emotional distress, many people withdraw emotionally from the people around them. This also means a withdrawal from one's Self. This withdrawal is thought to be part of a primitive survival mechanism called conservation-withdrawal. It consists of fright that causes an animal to go into a state of paralysis. It poisons relationships and can evolve into paranoia if left unchecked. Trust is re-established over time by consistent, caring, empathetic persons. It is the glue of human relationships. It is often vital to have face-to-face interactions to build trust because emotions are better understood nonverbally than verbally.

Valuing Self-Determination

Self-determination is almost uniformly cited as vital to recovery. This is the difference between a person managing their own life and relying on others to manage their life. Unfortunately, when people make bad decisions, society authorizes the mental health system to become responsible for their decisions. This paternalistic relationship, important at times of crisis, often persists beyond the time when a person once again is capable of making their own decisions. This, in turn, interferes with the constructive development of personal confidence and a sense of Self.

Connecting at a Deeply Emotional, Human Level

One person described her therapist as human, fallible, open to correction, and not god-like. Another person emphasized the importance of humor. It was very important that his caregiver, "Would keep me laughing when I saw him...he made me laugh."

There Is Always a Method to a Person's Madness

When we say that someone is crazy we usually mean that they make no sense and their actions and words are irrational. But, in fact, there is always a method to what is considered madness. What is missing is an understanding of the meaning beneath the apparent madness. Dr. Bertram Karon provided a good example in a description of his therapy with a man diagnosed with schizophrenia. One of the man's seemingly irrational behaviors was frequent bowing.

When Dr. Karon asked the man why he was bowing, the man replied that he was not bowing.

Dr. Karon demonstrated the bow and said, "But you do this, and this is bowing."

"I don't bow," the man repeated.

"What are you doing?" Dr. Karon asked.

"It's balancing."

"What are you balancing?" Dr. Karon asked.

"Emotions," the man replied.

"What emotions?"

"Fear and loneliness," the man replied.

When he was lonely he wanted to get close, so he leaned forward. But when the leaning forward got him too close to people and frightened him, he pulled back by straightening up. So what appeared to be irrational was actually a sophisticated physical manifestation of a complex internal struggle. With Dr. Karon understanding these movements, the man recovered from psychosis.

Having a Voice of One's Own

When people lack a Voice and a sense of Self, they are more likely to experience severe emotional distress. I know of a woman who said that her paranoia disappeared when she was able to speak up to her boss regarding her concerns on the job. Additional research has shown that people can learn to cope with hearing disembodied voices when they feel stronger than their voices. When they have more of a Voice in their social environment and can more readily discuss the voices they hear with others, their emotional distress is diminished. This is the description of a larger Self, which can observe lesser selves and help direct them. The Hearing Voices Network has helped people live with their voices by discussing them openly in self-help groups.

Validating All Feelings and Thoughts

During one of my most distressed periods, I spent an incredible day with a friend who performed extraordinary support by staying with me and listening to my thoughts and feelings. She was able to just be with me and not judge me. Later she said there were things I said while I was in distress that did not make sense but I was a good friend and she felt it was important to be with me. She trusted me and still does.

Following Your Dreams

Pursuing a personal goal can greatly facilitate the recovery process. A woman I know, who had many prior, frequent hospitalizations, reported that pursuing her dream of helping other people had made all the difference in her life. As a result, she felt that she now had a reason to get up in the morning. Once again she felt that she had a purpose in her life. She became a residential counselor and has not had hospitalizations in several years.

Relating with Dignity, Respect, and Equality

One person in recovery reflected, "The key ingredients for me on my journey to recovery are: being treated with dignity and respect; having a mentor; and peer support from people who really understand my situation and who have been there." Another spoke of a doctor who meant a great deal to him, "He respects everyone, no matter who they are."

Just as I treat every person with respect regardless of their social status, I expect the same from every other person, however lofty their station in life might be. After all, as Bob Dylan said, "Even the president of the United States sometimes has to stand naked." Another illustration of the importance of equality was revealed to me in a dream. *In the dream, my friend Will and I are looking at inscriptions in a graveyard for aristocrats. We start laughing as we read that one of the members of a prominent family died from eating too many cheeseburgers. As we are doubled over with laughter, I notice that a policewoman and an older man are sternly marching our way. Will catches sight of them and runs saying that he knows he does not belong there. Though I also did not belong there, I face the duo. They ask me why am laughing. I point to the inscription on the gravestone. In reaction, the older gentleman declares that the inscription is not funny. He says, "This is my grandfather's grave and you do not belong here." I look him in the eye and with complete confidence reply, "I belong here. After all, there are as many generations in my family as in yours!" I woke at that moment, feeling greater self-respect, though realizing I could have been more respectful.*

Learn from Your Pain

As I emerged from years of numbness, I experienced the psychic pain that I had suppressed for many years as intense, crippling back pain. One day I suddenly found that I had such intense back pain that I could not walk. I tried every conceivable somatic therapy, such as Percocet, acupuncture, and heat. Yet none of these helped. A friend loaned me *Healing Back Pain*, a book by Dr. John Sarno. I was irritated that she thought a book could help when I had what I thought was a physical basis of the pain. In desperation, however, I started to repeat the phrases in the book:

Dr. Sarno's Twelve Daily Reminders

1. *Pain is due to Tension Myositis Syndrome (TMS); it is not a structural abnormality.*
2. *The direct reason for the pain is oxygen deprivation.*
3. *TMS is a harmless condition caused by my repressed emotions.*
4. *The principle emotion is repressed anger.*
5. *TMS exists only to distract attention from the emotions.*
6. *Since my back is basically normal there is nothing to fear.*
7. *Therefore physical activity is not dangerous.*
8. *And I must resume normal physical activity.*
9. *I will not be concerned or intimidated by the pain.*
10. *I will shift my attention from the pain to the emotional issues.*
11. *I intend to be in control, not let my unconscious mind be in control.*
12. *I must think psychologically, not physically, at all times.*

I had a little relief but still needed a wheelchair to get to a conference I was coordinating. Once I had given my talk at the conference, my back pain disappeared. I then realized that the pressure of organizing a conference had been like an unbearable weight on my back. Since then

I have often revisited these phrases when I have felt back pain begin to return. I find it especially important to ask myself, "What emotion am I experiencing which is the source of this back pain?"

Sarno's phrases could be written and applied to reframe distressing thoughts. Such phenomena are generally defined as symptoms of a mental illness, resulting from a chemical imbalance of the brain. So to shift our thoughts from a purely physical explanation to one that is psychological, consider this list:

Eleven Things to Remember About Psychic Pain

1. *Strange reality, such as the TV talking to me, is due to a "thought spasm" (TS) — a kind of one-theme thinking or monologue.*
2. *The direct reason for the TS is a fear of the unexplainable, which drives me inside.*
3. *TS is a psychologically harmless condition*
4. *TS exists to signal my need to integrate my trauma-fragmented self into a whole Self.*
5. *Since my brain is basically healthy, I have nothing to fear.*
6. *Therefore, continued thinking is not dangerous.*
7. *I need to stay connected to others and resume being open to new thoughts from others.*
8. *I will not be frightened by the TS.*
9. *I will shift my attention from fear to the reintegration of my sense of Self.*
10. *I intend to resume control of my life.*
11. *I must think in terms of psychological integration and social connections rather than in terms of a chemical imbalance of my brain.*

FIVE

The Empowerment Way
to Recover Your Life

My own understanding of recovery is rooted in the consumer/survivor/ex-patient movement that emerged in the 1970s as a part of the larger movement of civil rights for many segments of society that transformed the United States in the 1960s–'70s. My first exposure to this movement was the Network Against Psychiatric Assault Newsletter. Its editors, Leonard Frank and Wade Hudson, were based in the San Francisco Bay area and were pioneers in what was then known as the ex-patient movement.

> **A word on language.** Our movement has focused much attention on how we are described. Those people presently receiving services are called "consumers" and those who are out of the system have chosen to call themselves "psychiatric survivors." Overall, we prefer to be called people, just like everyone else. Some of us now refer to ourselves as "persons with lived experience of recovery." The struggle over how to describe ourselves emerges from political and existential conflicts. We want to define our experiences in our own terms. In fact, describing our experiences ourselves we feel is essential to our existence and our collective evolution.

Leonard and Wade were among the earliest voices to question the abuses of psychiatry. When I encountered their message, it resonated with me. They and other early leaders — such as Judi Chamberlin, Sally Zinman, Howie the Harp, Rae Unzicker, Ted Chabasinski, and Paul Dorfner — believed that by being labeled mentally ill, we were objectified and deprived of our rights. In Boston, The Mental Patient Liberation Front worked hard to protect the rights of mental patients. In 1975, they initiated *Rogers v. Okin,* a court case against the Department of Mental Health, which maintained that it was a civil rights violation to forcibly medicate mental patients. The Massachusetts Superior Court decided in favor of the plaintiffs. The state however, subsequently found a way to circumvent that decision by instituting a special guardianship for the purpose of forcibly medicating consumers. (Ironically, it is called a Rogers Guardianship, after Ruby Rogers, the lead plaintiff in *Rogers v. Okin.)*

These early leaders are my heroes. Judi Chamberlin, in particular, played a pivotal mentoring role in my development as an advocate. During those early years, Judi saw a need for those who had once been labeled with mental illnesses to come together and speak with a voice of our own. The title of her book is *On Our Own,* and the subtitle is *Ex-patient Controlled Alternatives to the Mental Health System.* She understood that we needed to take charge of our own lives and the programs that assisted us. The year after the publication of her book Judi attended the founding meeting for the National Alliance for Mental Illness (NAMI) in Madison, Wisconsin. The week following the meeting she wrote to Dr. Herbert Pardes, Director of NIMH. She said it was helpful for parents to have an advocacy group, but also cautioned him: "They do not, however, speak for those of us who are ex-patients. We need to speak for ourselves." Indeed, an early and continuing theme of our movement is the slogan used by the anti-apartheid movement in South Africa, "Nothing about us without us."

In 1981, I and several other ex-patients working as professionals within the system were invited to NIMH to share our thoughts regarding changes needed in the system. NIMH also suggested that we start a network of professionals with lived experience of recovery across the country. When I ran the idea past Judi, she reacted very negatively. "No, you should never start such a group, because it would undercut the power of the ex-patient movement." How wise she was. At the time I was disappointed. However I gradually came to see the wisdom in her view.

It took many years for the movement leaders to accept me as a fellow leader. My status came under special scrutiny because I was a psychiatrist, the most distressing personification of mental health abuse. In 1983, Judi and I and several other Boston leaders started the Ruby Rogers Drop-In Center. It became a model for other consumer-run social clubs across the country. The need for friends and support remains one of the most pressing needs for people in recovery from mental health issues. In 1992, Judi, Pat Deegan, Laurie Ahern, and I started NEC. Our intent from the beginning has been to establish a center run by persons with lived experience, which would serve as a source of understanding and addressing mental health issues from our perspective. Recovery through hope and empowerment has been a major theme of our center. Judi remained actively involved in NEC and the Center for Psychiatric Rehabilitation at Boston University until her death in 2010. We all miss her, but carry her spirit strongly inside us.

✻

Recently I had a dream, which encapsulated my present thinking about the broader scope of recovery:

> I am in a class. The teacher is giving a lecture on mental health. At the start of the lecture he is dressed in a suit. I and the other students are neatly arranged in rows all facing forward. Everyone is intently taking notes. Gradually, as the teacher is emphasizing the importance of small groups, he sheds his suit and appears in a South Pacific grass skirt. Even his facial features and expression change from stern, male, and professorial to cherubic, avuncular, and of indefinite gender. Then looking around I am amazed to see that the class has broken up into small groups that are dancing. The groups come to resemble small tribes inspired by the professor who have rediscovered some ancient ritual of connecting.

✻

I recall that six to eight termites are required to build an arch, which is the basic building unit of all their structures. I think that deep in each human is a need to relate in small tribes. It is my contention that a great deal of mental distress results from the fragmentation caused by traumas. These traumas lead to isolation and powerlessness. Recovery is best carried out in small groups, which come together in dialogical fashion and (re)create belonging and participation in the life of the tribe. I think that the most important arches that human tribes can build are arches of consciousness.

In summary, I believe recovery is an evolution in our consciousness, which comes through building arches of expanded consciousness via the dialogical participation in small tribes. These consciousness-raising tribes are able to come together to build larger wellness villages and communities. It is this evolution in consciousness that is being led by persons of lived experience of recovery.

We can now understand the evolution of the consumer/survivor movement in this fashion. In the beginning, about eight or ten brave, critical thinkers called upon their own lived experience, and started to regularly communicate about the abuses of psychiatry. They were centered in the major cities: New York, Philadelphia, Boston, Portland (OR), Berkeley, and San Francisco. They acted like termites of the spirit as they laid down the values of our movement. The arches of consciousness that they built emerged from heart-to-heart conversations within small groups of committed human beings, being human.

In 2012, a contingent within the consumer/survivor/ex-patient (C/S/X) movement in the United States who were working to create a definition of recovery established a set of five supporting principles. The following is the definition of recovery that received the highest number of votes (over 1,000) in a SAMHSA (Substance Abuse and Mental Health Services Administration) sponsored survey:

Self-determination, empowerment, and hope are vital to recovery because they are the avenues for finding our voice to become active participants in a society based on equality of access to jobs, housing, education, and health care. We are glad SAMHSA emphasizes trauma-informed, culturally-attuned, peer-delivered care for MH (mental health) and SA (substance abuse).

Principles of Recovery

We endorse the Western Massachusetts Recovery Learning Community's Guiding Principles for Recovery, which include:

- *Self-Determination and Choice*
- *Mutuality*

- *Optimism*
- *Respect*
- *Genuine Human Relationships*

We believe that all people are capable, have insight, and can live self-deter-mined, fulfilling lives.

※

What did I go through at age twenty-four if my experience was not primarily a result of a neurological chemical imbalance? As I meta-phorically proposed earlier in this book I think my experience — and that of many others like me — can be likened to that of being an emo-tional canary in the cultural cave of our society. I believe people who have severe psychological distress are better able to detect the cultural toxins in our society. It seems that my psychosis was an early warning both to myself and to those around me, that an over reliance on linear rational thought can lead to a dangerous degree of dehumanization. I had taken the classical objectification of reality to what appeared to be its logical extreme: looking at humans as machines.

Having friends who shared my concern about this limited form of thinking was essential to my recovery. First there was Jim. He spent a day with me during my last severe episode. Even today he marvels at the insights I revealed during my so-called ravings. He said, "They said you were crazy, but much of what you said made perfect sense." He recalls that I would point in one direction and say, "We could go in that direction." I would ask him if he thought that was the right direc-tion to go. He would agree that we could go in that direction. Then, I would point in the opposite direction and tell him the opposite direc-tion could be equally true. I pointed out there are a variety of equally valid directions to pursue. He said, even at that time, he could see my point. That validation was very helpful. I realize now that I was meta-phorically describing the course of my life. He could relate because he too had started out in the direction of being a linear scientist and instead decided on the path of an environmentalist.

Another friend spent an entire day with me while I was experienc-ing my last prolonged episode of an altered state. She later said, "It was unusual for you to spend time with me during the day. I was glad

I didn't have a deadline. We just went walking. You seemed content to go walking. I wasn't able to follow some of what you were saying but most of what you said reflected things I had felt at times also. There was no overlay." I told her I was very concerned about time, and had become convinced that time was "just a fabrication of our minds to keep us all working." I looked up and there was a huge digital clock announcing the advance of every second. When I raised this concern with her, she agreed. She said that was why she only used a watch to give her an approximation of time. She showed me her watch and I could see it was not set to the correct time. I also marveled that her watch had no numbers, and in fact its minimalist design displayed very few marks. She reflected, "I'm concerned that if I take time too seriously I will feel like Captain Hook in *Peter Pan*. He was followed by a crocodile that had swallowed a clock, and the incessant sound of the clock was a constant reminder of the passage of time." Her acceptance of my concerns and the commonality of our experiences eased my terror. It appears that it is not our unusual beliefs that often lead to madness, but it is the terror that these beliefs engender in others, which are intensified by the feeling that we are the only ones who have ever felt this way. Perhaps it is this sharing of reality that keeps us sane.

In the new era of healthcare reform, however, we need a broader concept of recovery, which can continue to give hope to those of us labeled with a psychiatric diagnosis, and which can also be understood by the rest of society. For instance, misunderstandings occur when persons with a variety of other disabilities cannot relate to the concept of recovery. They mistakenly think our concept of recovery means that people with autism will be able to relate socially like everyone else, or that people in wheelchairs will walk. **We have, however, explained to the leaders of the cross-disability movement that our values of recovery are consistent with their values of independent living, i.e., consumer control and consumer choice.**

To frame recovery more broadly, we must go beyond a narrow medical definition of mental health issues. For many years professionals and researchers have described mental health issues as illnesses characterized by a permanent biological defect and a chemical imbalance from which people rarely recover. In the eyes of this group, recovery would only occur if a cure of the defect were discovered. Countless research studies have been carried out to define the supposed biological basis of mental health issues. No consistent deficit has been found. At best it was believed that the illness could go into remission, during which time symptoms are managed. This is the maintenance model, which has left many people experiencing hopeless distress. In fact, on April 29, 2013, Dr. Thomas Insel, Director of NIMH, shocked the mental health field when he wrote in his public blog that NIMH would not use the DSM 5, because, "Unlike our definitions of ischemic heart disease, lymphoma, or AIDS, the DSM diagnoses are based on a consensus about clusters of clinical symptoms, not any objective laboratory measure." This is a sound critique of the biological model of mental health conditions, yet the rest of the field fails to pay attention. It appears that economic interests trump science.

Recovery Rates Are Higher in Developing Countries

Many components of the recovery culture that we are seeking in the United States can be found in those parts of the less-industrialized world referred to as the "developing world." In many ways, the industrial world appears to have lost touch with some of the fundamental values of community and relationships that the developing world still values. Even though the industrialized world has developed technologically, it is underdeveloped socially and culturally. Conversely, the non-industrial world is highly attentive to the social and cultural dimensions of community life. This valuing of social connections by persons in the developing world may be one of the central reasons why two studies by the World Health Organization have discovered that the recovery rates from psychosis are much higher in the developing world than in developed countries.

The Zulus provide an illuminating example of the importance of community building. They intuitively incorporate affirming dialogue as part of their daily life. Everytime a member of the tribe sees another member, they acknowledge the other's deep Self with an affirming greeting. When one Zulu greets another he says, "I see you," meaning, "I see the deep you." The other when replying, "I am here," is affirming that his personal deep Self has been touched. This sequence is then reversed. This greeting is an example of the practice of the philosophy of *ubuntu*, or appreciating the humanity in each other.

We should be diligently studying these societies to understand why their recovery rates are so high, especially considering that these countries used only 16% as much medication per capita as the industrialized world. Some people think that this lower use of medications is one of the reasons for higher recovery rates. People, also believe that a critical factor is greater community cohesion. The decline of community in American society has been well documented in popular works of sociology, such as David Riesman, Nathan Glazer, and Reuel Denne's landmark book *The Lonely Crowd,* and Robert Putnam's more recent, *Bowling Alone.*

Ubuntu places the highest premium on relationships, the crucial element toward creating a cohesive community. The South African philosopher, Dirk J. Louw, has told the story of black miners who regularly walked off their job for no apparent reason. When the elders of the village were questioned about this behavior they explained it was because the workers had to leave their *ubuntu* behind to go to work. In this case, *ubuntu* referred to their humanity, meaning that working in the mines robbed them of their intrinsic humanity. To the workers, their humanity was more important than their jobs. Could it be that in so-called developed societies many of us have had to leave our humanity behind as a price of industrialization? Unfortunately we have not found a way to preserve our humanity and continue with our breakneck pace of technological advance.

Is *Ubuntu* Related to High Recovery Rates?

Nelson Mandela once said, "A traveler through our country would stop at a village, and he didn't have to ask for food or for water. Once he stops, the people give him food and entertain him." This is but one aspect of *ubuntu*. *Ubuntu* encompasses an understanding that people should not enrich themselves. The bigger question is: Are your actions going to enable the community around you to improve?

Ubuntu gained international significance when South Africa's Truth and Reconciliation Commission declared it to be the philosophical basis for their treatment of those responsible for past violence under Apartheid. The 1997 South African Governmental White Paper on Social Welfare officially recognizes *ubuntu* as:

The principle of caring for each other's well being... and a spirit of mutual support... Each individual's humanity is ideally expressed through his or her relationship with others and theirs in turn through recognition of the individual's humanity. Ubuntu means that people are people through other people. It also acknowledges both the rights and the responsibilities of every citizen in promoting individual and societal well-being.

The following description comes from an essay by Dirk J. Louw entitled, "*Ubuntu* and the Challenges of Multiculturalism in Post-Apartheid South Africa:"

The basic value underlying ubuntu is captured in the Zulu phrase, umuntu ngumuntu ngabantu which translates (by Van der Merwe and Ramose) as: "To be human is to affirm one's humanity by recognizing the humanity of others in its infinite variety of content and form"... Ubuntu means a respect and valuing [of] the differences in others, which can only emerge through dialogue, or "mutual exposure."

Ubuntu also describes the process of a person becoming a full human being through their relationships with their community. Before being incorporated into the community of persons through person-to-person contact, one is regarded merely as an "it," i.e., not yet a person. Not all human beings are therefore persons. Personhood is acquired. Moreover, initiation does not only incorporate one into personhood within the community of the living, but also establishes a link between the initiated and the community of the living-dead or ancestors.

In a second essay, "*Ubuntu*: An African Assessment of the Religious Other," Dirk J. Louw further elaborates : "*Ubuntu*'s respect for the particularity of the other links up closely to its respect for individuality."

The Western view of individuality sees each person as an isolated, self-sufficient entity, separated from their community. "*Ubuntu* [according to Louw] unites the self and the world in a peculiar web of reciprocal relations in which subject and object become indistinguishable, in which 'I participate therefore I am' is substituted for 'I think therefore I am.'"

Ubuntu also is rooted in the concept that each person is a process of becoming, not a fixed or absolute entity in nature. As Louw writes,

"An *ubuntu* perception of the other is never fixed or rigidly closed, but adjustable or open-ended. It allows the other to be, to become." According to *ubuntu*, persons are both human *beings* and human *becomings*.

The concept of *ubuntu* resonates with the concept of dialogue. In African culture, there is a natural orientation towards conditions that facilitate dialogue: listening together, suspending a single belief, sharing and exchanging ideas, and making room for a variety of voices. In fact, a culture that supports the idea of many gods supports dialogue more than Western monotheism does.

Another example of healing through dialogue is found in the description of a community mourning ceremony in Pat Barker's novel, *The Ghost Road*. The main protagonist, the real-life psychoanalyst and anthropologist, Dr. William Rivers, attends a community healing ceremony of a tribe from a South Pacific island of Melanesia. The chief has died. Members of the tribe are sure they can hear the sound of the chief paddling his canoe out into the ocean. This listening together restores to the tribe a sense of cohesion that was temporarily interrupted by the chief's death. They also start to voice concern about strangers in their group: Dr. Rivers and his assistant. The community found its communal voice and *esprit de corps*.

Such community healing ceremonies, which are approximated in the Open Dialogue approach pioneered in Finland, are believed to be some of the reasons why developing countries show an increased recovery rate from psychosis. In fact, hospitalization in industrialized countries decreases opportunities for repairing mutuality, dialogue, and community essential to mental health.

In our culture, it is often a challenge to simply experience the present moment. An ability "to be in the here and now" requires letting go of permanence. Whenever I find myself saying, "This is the way I feel about my life at this time," I am also confident my life will change and evolve. Indeed, my view, luckily, is constantly evolving as I think and interact. This is essential to recovery because it is essential to life.

There is also another African concept of the world that has fueled my recovery. It is a conception of the universe as a perpetual and all-encompassing movement of sharing and the exchange of the forces of life. This is also akin to the Buddhist view *Neti Neti*. This little phrase, meaning "not so, not so," is repeated by Buddhists whenever they have a thought, so they do not overly attach to it and become captured by its limitations. This reality of the present moment is reflected in the writings of the Vietnamese Zen Buddhist monk and teacher, Thích Nhất Hạnh. "Life can be found only in the present moment. The past is gone, the future is not yet here, and if we do not go back to ourselves in the present moment, we cannot be in touch with life..."

This sentiment resonates closely with my experience of recovery. My last episode of breakdown/breakthrough enabled me to evolve beyond my over-attachment to the certainty of my ideas. I believe I needed to go through the breakdowns I experienced in order to see truths that I otherwise could not see. I had to break out of the habit of thought that said there was only one way to describe reality and that ideas were superior to emotions. Later, I will describe the ways that peer support and Open Dialogue facilitate an acceptance of uncertainty as a vital aspect of living. Perhaps through an increased use of these approaches, many more people will be able to make this breakthrough to a new way of being without needing to go through breakdowns.

In the years since my three hospitalizations, I have asked myself, "What happened to me? Why did it happen? How can I prevent it from happening again? How can I pass on those lessons learned to others?" I have realized that deep inside there was — and is — a true *me* yearning to emerge. As a young man, I thwarted its emergence. I was scarred by the traumas of my sexual abuse; my father's Huntington's disease; my having a 50/50 chance of getting Huntington's; my nearly dying of pneumonia, and my mother's depression. I was intent on making a great discovery in the lab, which would solve everyone's unhappiness and earn me a Nobel Prize. All other aspects of life seemed secondary. I was afraid to look people in the eye. I was afraid to open up and show my feelings. I was afraid of getting hurt or rejected or abandoned. That fearful part of me was afraid of living and it was saying 'no' to life. That false self was trapping my true Self in a protective monologue of hyper rationality.

As the "Self-Destroying Spiral of Fear and Death" diagram below illustrates, I was experiencing the dissolution of myself.

At the center of this inward spinning spiral, you can see that I was saying "no" to life. I only became aware of this when I finally could say "yes" to life. Though I did not actively attempt suicide, I was slowly

Self-Destroying Spiral
of Fear and Death

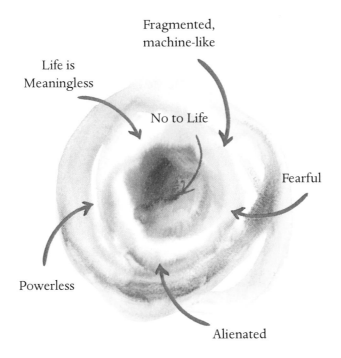

Fragmented,
machine-like

Life is
Meaningless

No to Life

Fearful

Powerless

Alienated

killing my inner Self. This is the point at which thoughts of suicide begin. In retrospect, it seems I had to go through dissolution of my old self because it was a false self. I believe I had constructed such an elaborate social self to conceal my deep Self. That social facade was the false self I had constructed by being "the good son and good student." My younger daughter went through such a transition in her senior year of college. She had just written a paper that her professor did not like. Ordinarily she had received A's, but in this case her teacher gave her a C. His note at the end of the paper indicated that she had not constructed the argument in the manner in which he thought she should have. However, she told me that rather than writing a paper that reflected what she thought the professor wanted her to write, for the first time she had composed a paper that she believed was the truth as she understood it. She said, "In the past, I have always been good at understanding what teachers have wanted me to say, but now I want to express what I see from my own unique perspective." Her final paper similarly reflected her truth. She never picked the paper up but she did pass the course. School is often the first social institution that trains many of us to become the self that our society expects us to be, rather than the true Self we are in our heart and soul.

When there is an interruption between one's Self and one's community, a person's spirit spins inward to form a protective shell. The inward spinning form is a type of inversion of the need of our life force to flow outward. This inward spiral can become a death spiral in which a death of Self is experienced. People often describe these inward spiral states as "mental illness." They can result in changes to one's chemistry. Generally however, I have found that the imbalances experienced during these periods are more a result of imbalances in one's life. Instead of attempting "better living through chemistry," we should pursue "better chemistry through living."

In Chapter Two, I characterized my Self-Destroying Spiral as a maelstrom of my spirit. Like the spiraling whirlpool in Poe's "The Descent into the Maelstrom," my false self was literally sucking the life out of me. Now I realize that this maelstrom of super rationality was strangling my feelings of life and spontaneity. Love is essential to our escape from such self-destroying spirals. This love occurs between us and others who are significant in our lives. The meditation I cited earlier captures the process of discovery of our life through stirring up our inner mute and hidden being:

Loving people means summoning them forth
            with the loudest and most insistent of calls:
it means stirring up in them
        a mute and hidden being
                who can't help leaping at the sound of our voice —
a being so new
                    that even those who carried him
                    didn't know him,

This book is about the theme raised in this lovely description of the importance of love. I came to these conclusions long after I had recovered. Each of us carries inside a mute being waiting to leap forth at the sound of the voice of those who love us. We can only come to know that inner being through another person who summons forth that being by their caring, understanding, and love. Often there needs to be someone other than a parent to draw forth that mute being. It seems to take a lover or a very good friend. In Chapter Eight, I describe a means of improving our capacity to connect with others in such a manner. We call this training eCPR. We can nourish that inner being by connecting with others who are capable of allowing that side of us to emerge, and by learning to be with ourselves in such a loving manner. This is a mutual process. We can also nourish our inner being by assisting another's inner being to emerge. In that case, our Voice calls forth our own inner being.

I experienced a dream recently:

In it, a man felt the waves of the sea as they were washing over him. He could hear the crashing of the waves on the nearby shore. And then he felt that he and the sea were one. He could then see the outline of others in the sea. His form merged with those of others in a gentle flow and rhythm of the waves as they carried feelings from one to another. The people of the sea were at one moment distinct, and at another moment blended together into a wave.

It seems all matter has an urge to flow from particles to waves. Growth, development, becoming oneself, and finding our authentic Voice may all involve this flow from our body to our spirit through our connections with life all around. A healthy, whole life occurs when there is such a flow between one's Self and one's community. There is a resonance that amplifies the life forces in each of its members, like yeast that enables bread to rise. One's self-esteem and creativity expand like a spiral. In such a state, one's life and spirit feel full, like a cornucopia. One experiences a sense of wellbeing. This interconnectedness is similar to the idea of *interbeing* described by Thích Nhất Hạnh.

There is an art to living because it is the most creative act that we participate in every day. The art of living is the art of recovery. Recovery means finding that kernel of life inside, and saying "yes" to it. Recovery begins when we can turn the death spiral into a life-affirming spiral as shown below. Later we will explore how emotional dialogue, generated by eCPR and Open Dialogue provide the loving relationships that nourish the new life needed to help this transition from fear to hope.

Self-Building Spiral of Life and Hope

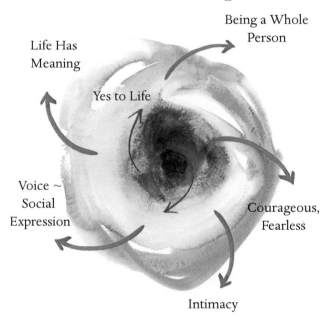

Being a Whole Person

Life Has Meaning

Yes to Life

Voice ~ Social Expression

Courageous, Fearless

Intimacy

This self-building spiral is consistent with John Weir Perry's description of psychosis as an active, creative attempt by a person's deepest Self to reintegrate. Trauma and uneven development cause some people to feel fragmented or divided inside. There may be parts of themselves they feel they cannot accept. When I was younger, I felt my emotional side should be suppressed; it felt dangerous for me to express it. This meant I did not know who I was. I felt numb and empty, like a robot. My extreme emotional states often were quests to understand who I was. Was I Einstein? Was I Christ? I wanted recognition. I wanted to know that my existence counted.

It was vital that I found people who could validate that my life was worthwhile. My therapist Dr. Semchyshyn always seemed to take an interest in me. It was also vital that he was authentic, because his acceptance presented a terrific example that I, too, could be authentic. It often requires someone who has been through a similar life changing experience to help others; a peer who can immediately connect and relate. In my darkest hours what I most wanted was for someone to say, "I understand. I went through a similar experience and learned and grew from it." Dr. Semchyshyn had experienced harrowing traumas as a child.

A positive attitude from a peer, therapist, or family member is vitally important. This approach communicates a sense of faith in life to the person in distress. This conveys a belief in their capacity to live a full life and the possibility of a meaningful future. These are the fundamental values of recovery. Dr. Perry notes the importance of the relationships around the person. If people providing assistance are frightened of someone in distress, they will transmit their fears, which, in turn, will only intensify the fears of the person in need. On the other hand, invaluable help can be provided when someone is comfortable being with a person experiencing other realities without feeling they must change them. When a person assisting is able to be with a person in distress deeply and fearlessly, he/she can allow the person to learn to be comfortable with his or her own unusual thoughts. Many peers have learned to accept unusual parts of themselves and in turn, they can convey emotional empathy and acceptance to others in need. A similar relationship exists when former drug or alcohol users act as counselors to active users.

My uncle Tremaine was a good example of someone who was able to provide help through a relationship that conveyed belief in another. He was a doctor of internal medicine. He had been trained by my father and practiced my father's brand of medicine. Shortly after his retirement at age eighty-five, I asked him why he had retired as he was still in good health and sound mind. He said that the clinic at Vanderbilt, where he had been a dean, was no longer interested in his approach to medicine. He said he ran few tests and only provided medication to 15% of his patients. He believed he could determine who needed medication by studying a patient's history and conducting a physical examination. He also made sure that each patient called him later in the week. He had a deep faith in each person's innate capacity to heal. He expressed regret that modern medicine had become too focused on the technological aspects of diagnosis and treatment. He was much beloved in Nashville and when he died ten years later, hundreds of grateful patients and former students attended his funeral. He was a role model for me, and indeed I recall that during my second hospitalization I heard his voice several times soothing me with reassuring words that I would get through my distress.

Initially, during the first years of the recovery of my humanity, I found it hard to live in such intensity. But in time, I came to appreciate the realization that only by valuing every moment, could I live fully. I came to understand that the emergence of the *me* that had been there all along changed how I saw myself and the world around me. This emergence reversed the flow of how I experienced the world. Prior to these breakthroughs, I would stand back, plan, and reflect before taking action. This was the period of my false self, trapping me in my maelstrom of fear. Then I rejected planning and dove into action with little thought. Neither course was satisfying. Finally, after my "Castle Dream" and my last major breakdown/through, I reversed the maelstrom of fear into a hurricane of hope.

The hurricane of hope diagram below shows a reversal of the flow from an inward, death spiral to an outward, life-affirming spiral.

That point of change happened dramatically during each of my extreme emotional states. The change deep inside me is similar to what Austrian psychoanalyst, Ernst Kris, termed "regression in service of the ego." I feel I had to return to a very early, preverbal state of infancy to integrate parts of myself that I had fragmented. Now I feel and think at the same time through an internal dialogue of my thoughts and feelings. Now when my heart talks to me, I listen very carefully. I reflect on what my heartbeats say and communicate to my heart that we can collaborate. This internal dialogue is the source of my heartbeats of hope. I feel more in control of myself and feel I can relate in a more genuine fashion. Thinking and feeling together give greater life to all that I do. At that turning point, I transformed my fear and anger towards life into a passion for life. This is where empowerment began. In Chapter Seven, I describe how this transformation is vital to finding our Voice. This turning point also is what we seek in assisting people in distress through eCPR.

Empowerment Way of Life Recovery

I know firsthand that there are times when people experience extreme distress. There are times when people immerse themselves within their own personal realities to protect themselves from harsh external realities. I contend, however, that naming that distress an "illness" interferes with understanding the source of the distress. We discover ways to recover through an understanding of what the distress tells us about ourselves. Using my lived experience and that of others, I will describe my present understanding about how such distress can lead to a break with day-to-day reality. By exploring this experience in depth I have been able to better understand the process of my recovery. At NEC, we have redefined mental illness as "periods of severe emotional distress during which it becomes more important to retreat into personal reality than to engage in the shared reality of one's expected social role." This definition is part of our "Empowerment Paradigm of Recovery, Healing, and Development."

I find it most useful to understand recovery by starting at the beginning of our life experience. As a newborn, we are in a state of connection with our mother, during which she experiences our inner being and we experience hers. These moments of intersubjectivity are the basis of our growth and development into conscious, communicating beings. We might call them shared moments of meaning. They involve a deeply felt connection, and establish an inner gauge of all subsequent experiences, such that we are always asking ourselves, "Is this person fulfilling my need for a similar lived experience?" This wish to re-experience a deep state of being with someone becomes a prime motivation of later behavior. Most likely it impels us into love, into work that fulfills such feelings, and dreams that take us to such a place. These moments of shared meaning are the expression of fulfilling dialogue at a deep level. It is the source of our vitality.

Losses and traumas interfere with these shared moments of meaning. We are frustrated and angry that our most basic need for connection is not being met. We experience emotional distress. Usually, we are able to heal from these periods. If, however, we have not established a strong sense of Self, we are unable to heal and we become distressed. We know inside that we need to return to an earlier way of being, to meet those needs for connection. Our mind can play tricks on us, and we can attempt to experience the world as we did when we were much younger, when we were more connected to the people in our world. We withdraw from the reality around us because it appears to be a wasteland. We look at television and try to receive from it special meaning intended for us and us alone. Our thoughts become louder and seem to take on a life of their own. At those times, a great deal of one's relating is preverbal. This is particularly so during periods of severe distress. I vividly recall the period a month prior to and during my second hospitalization, when I refused to speak. In fact, I reached a point where I could no longer speak, even when I wanted to. I had a heightened perception of the people around me, especially through nonverbal communication. I withdrew deeply inside because I had lost trust in those around me. I had also just experienced a failure in another love relationship. The pain from the loss was intolerable. Eventually, with the assistance of a chain of people who stayed with me in a deeply humane manner, I was able to crawl out to my recovery. I doubt that I could have returned to the land of shared verbal and cognitive reality without the assistance of these caring people. They literally saved my life.

Personal assistance based on a human connection can help bring a person back to shared reality. The nature of that helping relationship is similar to the quality that psychologist Carl Rogers cited as crucial for therapy: "congruence." For the helping persons to be congruent, they need to project their real and genuine human nature so that they can resonate in the present moment deeply with another person. It seems that this experience of human resonance is universal and appears in all cultures. **Recovery, to me then, is recovery of a life filled with the fullness of spirit that comes through sharing these resonating moments**. These moments are similar to what the American psychiatrist Daniel Stern defines as intersubjectivity: "the desire to know other people and to make one's self known to them that pushes humans towards intimacy and belonging." He calls those seconds in which two people intuit each other's thoughts and become conscious of it "moments of meaning," the essence of intersubjectivity. Intersubjectivity can only be understood in the context of "now," the one to ten seconds it takes humans to process an event into conscious experience. This idea is similar to Bahktin's belief that life is a chain of "once occurring moments."

Over the last twenty years, my colleagues and I at NEC have been developing a paradigm of recovery. At first we called this the Empowerment Model of Recovery. Then we realized that it was more understandable when we connected the recovery experience to development and healing. Also we changed the name from a model to a paradigm to indicate it is more a philosophy than a set of programs.

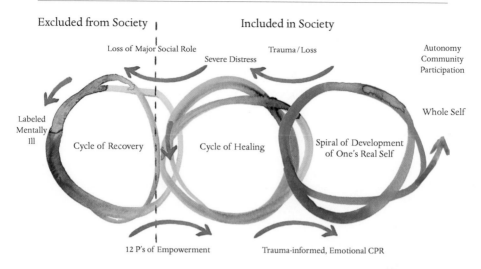

Excluded from Society | Included in Society

Loss of Major Social Role | Trauma/Loss | Autonomy Community Participation

Severe Distress

Labeled Mentally Ill

Whole Self

Cycle of Recovery | Cycle of Healing | Spiral of Development of One's Real Self

12 P's of Empowerment | Trauma-informed, Emotional CPR

Empowerment Paradigm of Recovery, Healing, and Development

The diagram above is our Empowerment Paradigm of Recovery, Healing, and Development. Our description begins with the circle on the right side of the diagram, which we call "The Spiral of Development of One's Real Self."

Spiral of Development

Our view of development is partly based on the work of Erik Erikson. Erikson's description of the phasic crises in psychosocial development has great meaning in our paradigm. Many people are diagnosed with severe emotional distress during their late teens. According to Erikson that is the period of identity formation. It is a necessary step towards being able to establish intimacy. If this step is not completed, the person relates superficially, experiences identity diffusion, and is more vulnerable to emotional distress. Harvard developmental psychologist Robert Kegan has viewed the development of a person's Self as proceeding in a spiral fashion. Kegan posits that our sense of Self evolves over a lifetime through experiencing increasingly complex cultures, which act as "holding" environments.

The first holding culture of life is being within our mother's womb. This is followed by the cultures of family, school and then work. These stages in development each involve a unity and a separation from the previous level. So too in our model of recovery, the emotional distress often is an opportunity for a new developmental step towards greater autonomy and self-determination as an adult. What is called "mental illness," then, can be considered an attempt to solve issues interfering with meeting the cultural expectations for a certain developmental phase. The Empowerment Paradigm is also consistent with the positive psychology of Martin Seligman and Mihaly Csikszentmihalyi, and Self-Determination Theory of Edward L. Deci and Richard M. Ryan.

These latter psychologists have emphasized that development depends on the active participation of the person as an actor in his/her life. Recent research by Ryan and Deci has shown that people are motivated to a greater degree by a wish for autonomy, competence, and connection, which enable them to gain greater control over their life, than by externally supplied rewards and punishments. Building relationships of trust and understanding are vital to gaining greater control over one's life. People need other people to gain the skills and resources that enable them to live an autonomous, self-regulated life. No man indeed is an island. In other words, community integration is an integral aspect of developing a whole Self. Through these loving relationships, each person truly comes to know her/his unique dreams and plan a life full of motivation and meaning. This increased self-knowledge deepens consciousness and extends one's autonomy. People work through stresses, losses, and their imperfect fit within their community. They become architects of their own life and in so doing develop an empowered, hopeful Self. Through this healthy spiral of development, people are able to find meaningful work and build a home of love through their network of mutually supportive family and friends.

Spiral of Healing

If, in the course of a person's development, there is a combination of trauma, loss, a poor fit with one's environment, and insufficient supports, there is an interruption in this development. Individuals with traits or characteristics that are not accepted by their community are more likely to experience this interruption in their development. The cultural norms of a particular society determine which traits and people are rewarded and which are rejected. The degree of acceptance of a person's traits is frequently a function of the lack of tolerance by a society rather than a lack of the individual's capacities. For instance, children with more visual, gestalt learning styles may fail in schools where children are expected to be aural, linear learners. In their frustration, they often experience severe emotional distress, unexpressed anger, and loss of control over their behavior. They are then diagnosed as hyperactive, medicated, and often segregated from other children. They may fail to form relationships, learn social skills, and gain the resources needed for their development. If they can share these feelings with significant authentic people, the unexpressed emotions can be transformed into passion. This can be done through eCPR, which is a trauma informed approach.

Often, for people with psychiatric and physical impairments, peers can be supportive by sharing their experiential knowledge in a non-stigmatizing fashion. It is also vital to alleviate the source of their frustration by finding a more accommodating learning environment. Healing then enables people to resume their spiral of development through a belief in themselves and by connecting with an accommodating social and learning environment. In so doing, they regain control of their lives. The environment needs to accommodate to the needs of the individual as much as the individual needs to adapt to the expectations of their community. At various times in their lives, nearly everyone goes through some aspect of this cycle of adaptation and accommodation. The more often people and their environments go through this cycle, the less vulnerable they are to becoming mentally or physically disabled. A good example of a community accommodation is in Gay Head, Massachusetts, where a large number of people had a hearing impairment. Rather than forcing those people with a hearing loss to adapt by speaking, the community learned sign language.

Spiral of Recovery from the Label of "Mental Illness"

If people are unable to adapt, and their environment is not sufficiently accommodating for them to fulfill their expected social role, "symptoms" appear. These "symptoms" are important messages from deep within, which tell the person and those around them the nature of the problem between the person and their environment. All too often, the person in distress is blamed rather than the environment. Then they need to tell themselves stories of their great-imagined accomplishments to overcome their rejection. Often this results in hospitalization or some other form of psychiatric institutionalization in which the person's life is placed under the control of others. Very frequently this process is involuntary: few people voluntarily give up that degree of control over their lives. The combination of an interruption of one's capacity to determine one's own life, severe emotional distress, and an inability to fulfill one's expected social role results in the person being labeled as "mentally ill." I use quotation marks around the phrase "mental illness," to indicate that I do not think of it as an illness like diabetes. I nonetheless use the term because it is a familiar label. In addition, it is a label, which has powerful social consequences. The form the "mental illness" takes depends on the stage of a person's development when the interruption occurred. People who are past high-school age and who are unable to work for an extended time due to severe emotional distress are further labeled "psychiatrically disabled." They are institutionalized either in actual institutions or in a segregated life in the community.

NEC defines "recovery" as the resumption of (or establishment of) participation in the community in a social role other than "mental patient." **Recovery means regaining a major social role, such as student, worker, parent, or tenant, and the resumption of control over one's life. Recovery involves reconnecting, being believed in, and believing in oneself, as well as becoming empowered enough to resume one's "spiral of development."** By this paradigm, people can actually fully recover from "mental illness," although they still need to continue transforming and healing from trauma. They may need to continue to take medication and may need therapy, but they are the main decision-makers in their life. There are many in our society who take medication and receive therapy but are not labeled "mentally ill." The primary distinction between a person labeled "mentally ill" and a person labeled "normal" seems to be whether the person has experienced a major interruption in their development and life that resulted in others making decisions for them. **NEC distinguishes between rehabilitation, remission, and recovery.** *Remission* **is a medical term indicating that symptoms are reduced but one is still "mentally ill."** *Rehabilitation* **similarly means that a person regains their function** but is still "mentally ill." Recovery means that one is no longer labeled "mentally ill."

As mentioned earlier, in some languages the word recovery additionally alludes to the recovery of one's life or humanity. In that sense, the most devastating aspect of mental illness is that one experiences a loss of one's humanity during the course of a break down and labeling. In this context, it is understandable why the principles of the recovery movement focus on the most human aspects of our lives.

We want to be regarded and addressed as fully functioning human beings, not just labels. There are buttons imprinted with the slogan, "Label Jars Not People." We want a *person-first* language. We want to be seen in the richness of our individual culture and history, not placed in a category. We want to be seen in all the dimensions of our being, on the levels of mind, body, and spirit, not merely as a chemical equation. **We want to lead rich and fulfilling lives in which we are the architects of our existence based on our unique dreams and aspirations.**

We, the people with lived experience, characterize recovery from "mental illness" as living a full life within our community, where we can choose the services and supports that enable us to control our lives. These principles parallel those for the independent living movement for people with all disabilities. (See Chapter Four for the seven characteristics of someone who has recovered.)

PART III

Learning to Live through Empowering Dialogue

During the last forty years, people with lived experience and their allies have identified the most important principles of recovery. This movement has been especially prominent in the urban centers of the United States, Canada, New Zealand, Australia, and Europe. We have successfully advocated for recovery to be the vision for transforming the mental health system. Until recently however, we lacked a means of implementing recovery. Most clinical programs fall short because recovery must be individualized and person-directed. Quietly during this same period, in rural areas of Finland and Norway, small groups of dedicated mental health professionals have been developing a new approach to treatment. This approach has the potential of implementing the recovery principles conceived by persons with lived experience. This approach is called "Open Dialogue."

SIX

What Is Dialogical Recovery of Life?

For many years, I have been convinced that dialogue played a vital role in my recovery. I first read about dialogue in the works of Martin Buber and Paulo Freire in the 1970s. I often return to Buber's moving work, *I and Thou,* for inspiration. I discovered a new use of dialogue in 2007 while attending a conference in Ohio. A mental health administrator at the conference said he had been reading about how Dr. David Bohm had discovered that dialogue was important in generating new meaning. He appealed to mental health workers to engage in dialogue with consumers.

I studied Bohm's *On Dialogue* and started a series of meetings called "Recovery Dialogues" at our mental health center. Shortly thereafter, I discovered the Open Dialogue approach to psychosis developed in Finland. This approach to people experiencing a first-break psychosis was reporting highly successful results. Open Dialogue has created a great stir since its public introduction in the United States through Robert Whitaker's book *Anatomy of an Epidemic*, and Daniel Mackler's documentary film, *Open Dialogue.*

Mary Olson, an associate adjunct professor at the Smith College School of Social Work, is the only certified trainer of Open Dialogue in the United States. In 2001, she spent a year as a Fulbright Scholar at the University of Jyvaskyla, where she met Jaakko Seikkula, a member of the faculty and one of the developers of Open Dialogue. Already teaching dialogic-systems ideas, Olson teamed up with Seikkula on a study of Open Dialogue in 2003. Since then, they have continued to collaborate. Professors Olson, Seikkula, Doug Zeidonis, and I are developing a pilot study of this new approach at the University of Massachusetts Medical School.

I completed a 200–hour course on Open Dialogue taught by Professors Seikkula and Olson. They introduced me to the writing of the Russian philosopher and literary critic, Mikhail Bakhtin, who in 1929 described his concept of dialogism. Bakhtin wrote that dialogue is life and life is dialogue:

> *The dialogic nature of consciousness, the dialogic nature of human life itself. The single adequate form for verbally expressing authentic human existence is the open-ended dialogue. Life by its very nature is dialogic. To live means to participate in dialogue: to ask questions, to heed, to respond, to agree, and so forth. In this dialogue, a person participates wholly and throughout his whole life: with his eyes, lips, hands, soul, spirit, with his whole body and deeds. He invests his entire self in discourse, and this discourse enters into the dialogic fabric of human life, into the world symposium.*

Child psychologist Colwyn Trevarthen has shown that from the instant of birth, a mother and child are engaged in an intricate dialogue and dance of gestures. The following is my own description of the importance of connecting at a very deep level with my children, written when my daughters were ages fourteen and sixteen:

> *We all once blissfully floated in a dream world of our mother's embracing fluids. We could hear the gentle, rhythmic whoosh, whoosh, whoosh of her heartbeats. We could feel the firm, protective surroundings of her uterine wall as it massaged our growing bodies. Perhaps we tasted her salty fluids rich with nutrients and love. Is this not the appeal of the ocean? The rhythms of its waves remind me of her heartbeat. My mother's salts remind me of my salty waterbed in the ocean. When I immerse myself in the ocean, and feel the surging power of its swells, I feel at one with my deepest Self, the Self I experienced in my earliest existence. My deepest Self is whole and connected with all other beings. From the caressingly warm ocean of my mother's womb, I was rudely awakened alone in the cold glare of the dry, world outside. I feel I have spent much of the rest of my life yearning to re-experience the bliss of being.*

I seek bliss in many forms. I seek it in relationships with others and through art, play, and work. I can still recall the feeling of my newborn daughters wriggling up my belly as they tried to find their comfort zones. My wife and I would coo a gentle rhyme and rock them with a rhythmic beat. The harmonious play of lights and colors pleased them.

But I cannot hold them forever. They need to walk, swim, and speak as they travel into worlds beyond ours. They will return to have me help them, but they will be on their own power most of the time. I need to help them make this transition from their parents' home, and form their own lives. When I was coming of age, I needed to believe in my capacity to live my own life. I needed to believe in me. I needed others along the road who believed in my capacity to live my own life. Others who were not threatened by my leaving because they had a full life of their own. I needed to develop an inner soothing, an inner cooing, an inner whoosh, whoosh.

When I observed our babies, I would watch them rocking themselves and sucking on their hands. Soon, they coo. They learn to still their inner demons. Yet at times their cooing and rocking were not sufficient and they raised their voices. They fashioned their cry. Years later I can still feel the chills that my daughters' cries brought to my spine. Even today when they raise their voice I am right there as if it was still the middle of the night and some unknown horror was gripping their early life. I must check myself because I know today they no longer need me as immediately and deeply as they once did in those dark and lonely nights. But how much should I do for them? I am still on alert day and night. I keep my watch lest any harm should come to them. I try to be a lighthouse during their travels and travails. From a respectful distance, I try to provide a beacon of light to illuminate their dreams, while also warning them of any dangerous rocks. Though they are teenagers and are finding friends, music, and loves of their own, they need me more than ever to be ready to respond and reassure them that no matter how much anger we may express, we will always be able to connect at that deepest level. I taste their salty sadness as their boat ventures forth in my tears. For only the salt of my sea-born tears at times can soothe my pain of losing them as children as I know I must. My children have been such a blessing and I know I must survive the passing of their childhood just as I survived my own. I know I must survive so I can be there for them as they emerge on the other side of the water, just as a water skier emerges from the depths of the water. I know I must let them go so they can spread their wings and fly. Then they can fly back quickly when they need to know that they can once again venture out. Just as Harry Harlow showed with infant monkeys, the more nurturing the parent, the more adventuresome the child. I know that though I will lose a child, I will be delighted with the new person who shall emerge.

I now believe that my delusions were attempts to recreate that state of original natal bliss, and to feel connected to my deepest Self in the absence of deep relationships. They were attempts to fill the chasms and the emptiness I felt from being separated from a deeply loved person. When my first wife left me, I felt such a terrible void and loss that I had to fill it with some imagined being. When I believed the television was talking directly to me, I feel I was really trying to bring back some lost being. In less industrialized societies, members of a tribe come together to hear the whooshing sound as a recently departed loved one paddled their canoe into eternity. For them, the shared experience helped them restore wholeness to their community. The members of such connected tribes seem less likely to resort to individual delusions. This may be one of the reasons they recover from psychosis at a higher rate than those of us in so called civilized societies.

I recall with painful yet blissful vividness the words I used to describe the early moments of my first psychiatric hospitalization and my retreat into my own dream world:

I am lying on the hospital bed, listening to the rhythmic beat of the clicks of the intercom. I had been injected with Thorazine a day before and was in my own world, not wanting to come out. I hear the click of heels on the marble floor. I know that sound. Those are my mother's footsteps. I know she is nearby, though I will not open my eyes. I can feel a pattern of lights around me. I feel safe and at peace as long as I stay in my dream world. I refuse to wake up and I refuse to look at those around me because I would then be rudely jerked back into the painful world outside. I find out later that my mother did visit, but I would not respond when they tried to rouse me. They told her I was in a deep catatonic state and that I might never recover. Fortunately, after three days I did come back to consensual reality. [I may have been healing the trauma of nearly dying from pneumonia at age one.]

This retreat into a very deep inner world, which occurred on four occasions in my life, has been a great mystery to me. The more I have studied psychiatry, the more I have realized that few people have a good understanding of this process, which is called psychosis. I think the fear that a majority of others have of a person who is in such a deep withdrawal is a deep dread we all have that we might fall into such states of distress. I have written this book to try to unravel that mystery for myself and the world.

Dialogical Recovery of Life: Taking a "Dialogical Recovery of Life" approach to healing not only benefits the person who is experiencing extreme emotional states (clinically described as psychosis), but also aids the growth and healing of those around them. This applies to people experiencing states of lesser emotional distress, as well as to conditions of addiction. The following is a summary of ways that taking the Dialogical Recovery of Life approach can be of assistance to everyone who is involved in the experience.

Our lives grow through loving dialogues that create sparkling new narratives in all realms of our existence. When my life is lovingly nourished in all realms, I feel fulfilled and life has meaning. By *all realms* I mean that my mind, body, social life, and spirit are all enlivened by dialogue. In my physical realm, when my heart beats, when I breathe, when I sleep, and when I am awake, I experience rhythms of dialogue. My psychological realm consists of the interplay of thoughts and feelings, as well as cycles of planning, implementing, and evaluating progress towards my dreams. Social involvement in relationships of intimacy and friendship often cycle through intense and more casual phases. The most embracing realms of our existence are loving relationships with others in our community. These connections are life sustaining, and affect all the other realms. Relationships give a musical score to the opera of our mind and body and promote our overall health. Through these dialogues, we are able to break free from the master narrative of being powerless objects and construct our own "sparkling moments of empowered existence," as described by Michael White.

Proposal for Dialogical Recovery of Life after "Psychosis"

Origin

Dialogical Recovery of Life is a synthesis of: recovery values, emotional CPR, Open Dialogue, and trauma-informed approach.

Proposal

- Dialogue is the uniquely suited process for bringing renewed life to our Self and others. When we engage in loving, respectful relationships of astonishment through dialogue, we create space inside each other for new life and creations to emerge. Dialogue enables us to see our world, and the world around us through new eyes. This refreshingly broadened point of view enables us to dream and plan from our unique perspective.

- Trauma is any process that interferes with these life-sustaining dialogues and interferes with our will to live. Though we think of trauma as a *sudden* event that overwhelms our capacity to cope, the *ongoing* processes of invalidation and disrespect are often the most traumatic. Traumas cut us off from intimate relationships, and the nourishment of our personal growth.

- When our personal growth is impeded by trauma, we feel we are dying. It is one of the greatest pains one can experience. Therefore we do everything possible to heal and resume growth.

- To heal, we protect ourselves, often retreating to safety within. We seek healing through dreaming and reminiscing with the reserves of conversation we have stored within ourselves. This may be the function of dreams. This may be a reason that lack of sleep can lead to madness. If ordinary dreams do not solve our issues, we resort to daydreaming and creating works of art.

- If daydreaming and creating art do not heal our trauma, our minds employ one last emergency maneuver. Our imagination creates a virtual, deep monologue in an attempt to keep ourselves alive. In this state of monologue, we generate unusual thoughts and sensations referred to as delusions and auditory hallucinations. These are not symptoms of illness but courageous acts of life saving creativity. If this extreme condition renders us unable to cope, it is called psychosis.

- These imagined monologues are a manifestation of dialogue lost. Only one version of reality — our own — remains, and we fall into a death spiral. We often become suicidal, either passively by withdrawing from life, or actively by attempting to end the physical reminder that we are already dead.

- Drugs and medications are only a temporary way out of this death spiral. We may turn to drugs or medication to numb our pain, but the relief they offer does not last if we are not connected to those around us. (I am not opposed to medication, but have learned that thinking that the medications will fix a person distracts them and their supporters from the emotional connecting needed in recovery of life.) In fact, an over-reliance on "fixes" can accelerate the death spiral.

- Heart-to-heart, emotional dialogue, such as practiced in emotional CPR, is the only sustained way out of this death spiral. Living beings (humans, other animals, or plants) are needed to connect with the person who has turned inward. We need to engage in emotional dialogue with another living being in the present moment to escape the death spiral.

- Someone needs to resonate with the dying person's barely beating emotional heart. This resonating requires great attunement to one's own heartbeat of life. It often takes someone who has been there and found a way through. It takes someone with a strong will to live who can bestow hope to the person in despair. It takes a very human person who can fully believe in the other's capacity to recover their life. This is the essence of eCPR. This is why we call it heart-to-heart resuscitation.

- The Open Dialogue approach is well suited to re-establishing connections between the person in distress and their natural network. Just as eCPR helps a person to connect one-to-one with another person, Open Dialogue helps a person connect with their network.

⊙ Open Dialogue values the participation of multiple voices both between people and within people. This helps the person who has retreated into the certainty of their internal point of view to broaden their perspective and to see others' points of view.

⊙ Persons in distress first connect on an emotional level through the emotionally enriched communications of all involved. Then the person in distress can develop the trust necessary to accept other points of view.

⊙ Focusing on the present moment allows the person in distress to participate in the growing edge of reality of his/her unfolding social network.

⊙ By sharing the problems between the person in distress and her/his network, the person in distress feels less shame and blame, making it easier for them to participate. Power is shared by the person assisting sharing their expertise instead of entering as an expert, which enhances the empowerment of the person in distress and his/hers network. All these factors enable the emergence of a gathering in which each Voice is valued and heard.

• Using the dialogical approaches, of eCPR and Open Dialogue, improves the ability of all members of a social network to think clearly and flexibly. Many people who have experienced dialogical practices have noticed that their own thoughts became clearer through this process. eCPR and Open Dialogue can expand options and points of view by offering participants greater dimensions to their lives. In the interplay of dialogue, new meanings are generated that the participants had never previously dreamt of. This brings new ideas to life, which can then infuse lives with new purpose. This weaving together of different worlds goes beyond a single personal perspective and opens new horizons. Thinking more flexibly is vital to getting beyond delusions.

From Monologue to Dialogue

The most profound understanding that thinkers such as Buber, Bakhtin, Bohm, and Freire have grasped is that our personal growth occurs more through deep relationships than within the mind of each

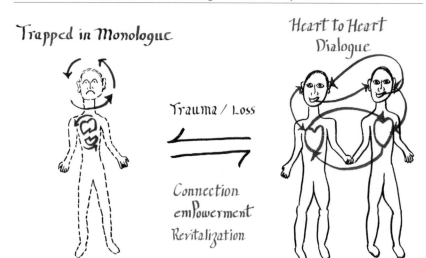

Trapped in Monologue

Heart to Heart Dialogue

Trauma / Loss

Connection empowerment Revitalization

individual. Buber stated this point eloquently when he wrote, "The innermost growth of the Self does not take place, as people like to suppose today, through our relationship with ourselves, but *through being made present by the other, and knowing that we are made present by him.*" Dialogue may seem simple, but it is hard to achieve. The theory of dialogue, as defined in the world of organizational development and as applied in mental health situations, posits that most of the time the majority of us live in a state of monologue. This means that we live within our own version of the world, which appears to us as the one and only version. Accordingly, we are usually more intent upon getting others to agree with how we see things than we are in learning things from others. These are discussions not dialogues. Fortunately, we can consider other points of view often enough to not get overly trapped in monologue.

In the illustration above, the image on the left gives a visual representation of what happens when we are so deeply involved in monologue that we cannot find a way out on our own. The figures on the right represent an ideal of human connectedness, a graphic representation of an *I-Thou* state of being. This pair is in dialogue with each other. These two people are best understood as embedded in a community of similarly loving relationships. They are connected equally at their heart and verbal levels. These relationships can be disrupted if there is trauma, loss, or any action that interferes with deep loving relationships. Then the person may retreat into her/his interior world and experience a fear of others. They become trapped in monologue, seeing only their version of the world repeatedly playing in their head. Their body appears as a dotted line because they do not experience their own existence very deeply; they lack a sense of "groundedness." The arrow back to connectedness is facilitated by eCPR.

When we are consumed in a state of monologue, we need to connect to others to return to dialogue. Yet that is also precisely the time when we are short on trust. When we are in a state of monologue, we have little capacity to see the whole being of ourselves or other people around us; we lack the wholeness that helps us understand what other people are really trying to communicate. Our thinking can become either too concrete or too abstract. We lose the dynamic interplay, which is vital to life itself.

In my own experience, my extreme focus on the chemical properties of one enzyme, specifically phenylalanine hydroxylase, sent me into a state of monologue. I could only consider one version of reality: my version. When this idea became fixed, I literally believed that everyone was a biochemical machine with no sense of self or self-determination. This left me feeling that my life was not worth living; I felt without a sense of purpose and powerless to affect the world. At times like this, symbols can become confused with the world they represent. At one time I was trapped with the fixed idea that everyone around me was a robot. I had become convinced that all reality could be explained in terms of its material properties. The logical conclusion was that all humans were robots. I could not, however, accept that I might be one. As strange as this idea may appear, it is notable that in recent years many movies and books have touched on this theme.

Unfortunately, there are people in the industrially developed world who exhibit some of the characteristics of robots. However, when I became consumed with this belief, it was at a time when I no longer was experiencing enough human interaction to distinguish the symbol from the reality. I was the victim of "either/or" thinking. Since then, I have learned that reality is not either the symbol or the material symbolized, but the relationship between both of them. Grasping this "both/and" quality of reality enables me to engage in dialogue. States

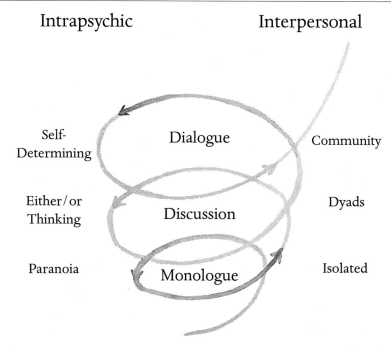

Intrapsychic   Interpersonal

Self-Determining Dialogue   Community

Either/or Thinking Discussion   Dyads

Paranoia   Monologue   Isolated

of mind that allow me to simultaneously grasp multiple versions of reality facilitate my capacity to enter into dialogue and community. Conversely, by engaging in dialogue it is possible to live with the uncertainty of "both/and" realities.

The above drawing shows in spiral form a person's development from monologue and isolation to dialogue and mutual relationships. On the left is a description of the evolution of a person's thinking and feeling, which is developed by engagement in community through reciprocal relationships. This description also helps us to understand why peer support is vital. Professional assistance alone often cannot help persons trapped in monologue. Mutual connection with peers is often a first step to community integration. The right side of the drawing is a visualization of how the development of a sense of Self, and evolving from monologue to dialogue, work in tandem. By moving into dialogue our sense of Self grows from an image of the world formed solely from the interior vision of our own eyes to a much more diverse and flexible view of the world through a variety of perspectives. **Exposure to people from diverse backgrounds is a vital aspect of developing a more tolerant understanding of people.**

The people who pioneered the Open Dialogue approach in Finland posit that psychosis results from a breakdown of dialogue within a social network. A person may manifest this loss of dialogue by producing utterances that seem to have little meaning, but which are, in fact, an expression of a systemic failure to communicate dialogically. When skilled practitioners restore dialogue within someone's social network, the person in acute distress experiences an increased ability to focus, and the extreme emotional states of psychosis disappear.

The developers of Open Dialogue may have found an explanation for Mikhail Bakhtin's description of the devastating effects resulting from a loss of dialogue. Bakhtin wrote, "For a human being nothing is more terrible than a lack of response." This is because, according to Bakhtin, "Life is dialogue and dialogue is life." To live is to participate in dialogue, and conversely, to lose dialogue means to feel one is dying. If we think of dialogue as the source of our life, then Bob Dylan was a dialogical philosopher when he said, "Whoever isn't busy being born, is busy dying."

Dialogical Recovery of Life from Monological Medicine

Note: In this book the term Open Dialogue is used to refer to both the specific practice of Open Dialogue in Tornio, Finland, and adaptations of dialogical practices in other areas of the world.

Why has Open Dialogue spurred almost viral interest, especially among people with lived experience? Great interest has been generated because of accounts of extraordinary outcomes reported by the group of Open Dialogue practitioners in Western Lapland, Finland. During two decades of utilizing this approach in that region, the frequency of schizophrenia went from one of the highest in the world to one of the lowest. These results were achieved by using a community-based, social network approach for young people experiencing their first psychotic episode. More than treatment specifics, however, the philosophy underlying Open Dialogue accounts for its great appeal to persons with lived experience. In fact, Jaakko Seikkula emphasizes that Open Dialogue is a philosophy based on principles and values, and not a program, *per se*. Such a distinction may seem esoteric to Americans, who tend to focus on reproducible protocols defined in manuals. In contrast to most American professionals, those of us Americans with lived experience have had a deep mistrust of established programs that insist on fidelity to a single model. An approach based on values rather than programs is more appealing to those going through recovery because it allows for agency and empowerment. **Most of us with lived experience feel that the most important element of recovery is empowerment: having a voice in decisions that affect one's life.** Programs and protocols intrinsically prevent recipients from developing agency and empowerment, whereas a philosophy based on principles and values leaves room for each individual's interpretation.

Dialogue has slowly been gaining a presence in the United States in other ways. At the very time that professionals in Finland were developing Open Dialogue, peers started using a dialogical approach here to improve communication between groups having difficulty understanding each other's point of view. In the early 1990s, I engaged in a series of such dialogues sponsored by the New York Office of Mental Health, which brought together professionals with lived experience and psychiatrists. Similarly, SAMHSA carried out a series of such dialogues. In addition, in the 1980s the eminent physicist David Bohm conducted a series of dialogues to help all concerned gain a deeper understanding of the implicit levels of reality. These Bohm Dialogues have had a profound influence in the business world.

The essence of Open Dialogue is the creation of a space between people that allows for the free, mutual, and creative generation of new thoughts and emotions. According to the Finnish psychologists, psychosis results from a person retreating into monologue — into his/her own world. In a world of monologue, there are very few new ideas. As the person loses touch with the people around them, they no longer are in touch with the shared reality of their community. Then the person in distress's thinking is described as delusional. Of course, if the community surrounding a person is constructing a destructive reality then withdrawal from that reality may be necessary for preserving life. **Unfortunately, our present day mental health system, by isolating itself from the new ideas of persons with lived experience, is trapped in its own monologue of hopelessness.**

When I experienced trauma as the result of loss of a love relationship, and loss of meaning in my lab work, I retreated into complete monologue. I only felt the safety to emerge from my monologue when a corpsman, the lowest ranking member of the team, created a dialogical space between us through nonverbal communication. This space has been described by clinical psychologist and family therapist, Peter Rober, as the "space into which life can come." This is the space that I believe our peer movement has been creating on a national scale through advocacy for recovery. Our collective lived experience has taught us that the essence of recovery is being able to live a free and fulfilling life in the community — a life in which we are the authors of our destiny. I call this approach "creating a dialogical recovery space," which enables us to live more fully.

The liberating life forces of dialogical recovery, however, face heavy resistance from the dominant, narrowly applied, new medical model. The older medical approach, as practiced by my father and his generation of doctors, was more respectful of the patient's participation in their healing. Those doctors made house calls and understood that healing involved the person and her/his social network. It was more dialogical. Without high-powered medical technology, these humble doctors would admit that, though doctors dressed the wound, the person's own powers and his/her loved ones did the healing.

I am not opposed to modern technology and medications, when used sparingly. In fact, penicillin saved my life. But many present day health care professionals exhibit an arrogant belief that they cure illnesses. Whether in mental health or physical health, medications can help relieve distress, but healing ultimately results from the coordinated agency of the person's whole Self. That Self is a combination of mind, body, and spirit in connection with the person's social network. I believe the narrow application of the medical model is perpetuating monologue. The medical model keeps many persons in distress and their network of family and professionals within the negative spiral of their own world. I call this dominant narrative of emotional distress the "monological medical model."

The following table shows how the principles and values of recovery are similar to the principles and values of Open Dialogue. In addition, it also shows how the dictates of the monological medical model contrast with these other sets of principles and values.

RECOVERY AND OPEN DIALOGUE PRINCIPLES COMPARED TO MEDICAL MODEL

DIMENSION	RECOVERY	OPEN DIALOGUE	MONOLOGICAL MEDICAL MODEL
Power	Empowerment is vital to recovery because persons in distress need to play an important role in all decisions in their life; they are experts in their own life	Power is shared by validating the interpersonal reality of the person in distress and by planning only with the person in distress present; therapists have expertise but not expert status	The provider exercises power over the person in distress by labeling person as their diagnosis and making plans for them without them
View of the person	Respecting the value of the person as a full human being, not a category or object	Valuing the contribution of the person in distress, which helps the person in distress feel whole	The person in distress is reduced to a diagnosis and a set of impersonal chemicals to be managed
Nature of the Concern	Persons in distress have lost or not yet found their Voice, their sense of Self, their purpose, their connections at an emotional level	The person in distress has retreated into monologue relative to their social network	The person in distress is a problem to be solved; an imbalance of neurotransmitters independent of the environment
Nature of solution to problem	Recovery of the person's humanity and participation in community through principles of recovery which can be aided by choosing medication	(Re)establishment of heart-to-heart dialogue with significant persons in their social network, medication may be a choice	Restoration of chemical balance through life-long administration of medications by professionals
View of future	By seeing examples of people who have gone through similar problems and recovered (peers) they regain hope.	Even the most severe issues are seen as being resolved by the network and team of therapists	Truncated future consisting of maintenance on medication under direction of professionals

I propose that a shift to a recovery-based, community healthcare system could be greatly facilitated by the adoption of a dialogical recovery philosophy. This would mean an infusion of dialogical principles and values into all facets of daily living. This could be best carried out through teaching everyone eCPR, and then engaging all the members of society in various sized dialogues, covering a variety of topics of great concern. In the healthcare field, for instance, we need more dialogue among persons with lived experience of mental health issues, substance use, and physical health issues, with psychiatrists and medical doctors. If such a dialogue occurs at the moment when the person in need is gaining a sense of their own agency, the result will be an invaluable integration of life experiences, knowledge, and diverse points of view. Once someone gains a Voice in their life, they can achieve genuine person-centered, whole-health planning.

SEVEN

Finding Our Voice

Many of us go through the motions of life and observe others' lives from afar. We are alienated from our deepest Self, the source of our Voice. The following description illustrates the devastating effect on Lauren Spiro of losing her Voice and the beginning of her recovery upon finding her Voice.

Locked in a seclusion room at the age of sixteen with a diagnosis of chronic schizophrenia, Lauren thinks back, was a metaphor of her locked in life at that point. She felt trapped, alone, caged and desperately wanted to belong, to feel she had a meaningful role in community. Her heart and values pulled her one way, while the culture around her pulled in the opposite direction – towards conforming to roles and principles that didn't reflect her deepest yearnings. She became lost in the void between these two overwhelmingly conflicted worlds that never ceased tearing her in opposite directions. Lacking resources and supports that she could trust to assist her in understanding and reconciling these opposing forces, the tension built until it boiled over. The boiling-over bypassed the usual cognitive channels, and instead came out as delusions. The content of the delusions, however, reflected verbatim the very conflict she was trapped in. She needed to feel that her life mattered, that she mattered; she needed meaning and purpose that genuinely reflected her Voice. And she couldn't find it. One night – everything changed. That sleepless night in a 9 x 9 foot white barren cell with bars on the windows, she decided that she could no longer bear the pain (of "schizophrenia") and gave herself permission to end her life — to end the torment. Ironically, that decision lead to the opening of a new door. She realized that if one option was death, then it made sense to put every ounce of energy she had to focus on finding a life worth living. To find that life she knew she had to reconstruct herself and stop listening to the endless screaming voices and images in her head. She thought that would make surviving another day possible, bearable. That night, unbeknownst to her at the time, was the beginning of her road to recovery.

Here is a description of losing my false voice and, in despair, finding my true Voice.

I had to go to the depths of my existence to decide if my life was worth living. Having been a dutiful son who carried out my family's expectations, I found myself at age twenty-four without any sense of living for myself. I had achieved much but I was living my life for others. I had no idea how I felt. I was pure thought and no feeling. My heart had stopped talking to me. I was only aware of being too angry to continue living my current way of life. Like Martin Luther, I said to myself, "This is not I!" The biggest step of my recovery was to say to myself, "Stop acting and just be."

To do so, I stopped going to my job in the neurochemistry laboratory where I was attempting to discover the chemicals responsible for feelings. The chemicals did not define my feelings. The job was not me. I stopped talking, because the words were always ones I used for others. I even stopped moving because all movements seemed alien, not my own. From this very quiet, self-observing place, I decided I would only emerge when I could express the Voice that was uniquely my own. It was a corpsmen, the lowest ranking aide, who reached me through nonverbal communication.

My next step in recovery occurred when I could transfer my anger from a stubborn 'no to life' to a 'yes to life'. It came in stages and first occurred when I was trapped in seclusion and vowed that I would humanize the mental health system so that everyone similarly suffering could recover. Then my anger became my passion and purpose. This was my deepest Voice speaking to me. It seemed that the only way for me to be freed from the delusion that others were controlling my life, was for me to truly gain a Voice by which I controlled my own life.

British clinical psychologists, Chris Harrop and Peter Trower, have written that, "The life-long experience of being intrusively controlled and of having an alien, not an authentic (self-constructed) self and the concomitant loss of a center of initiative, is likely to cause profound dysfunction in the normal operation of consciousness...and account for some of the anomalous experiences of psychosis." In other words, if a person is not able to develop a strong, centered, authentic Self, they have the types of disturbances of consciousness, which can cause them to lose touch with reality and become psychotic. Harrop and Trower propose that development and recovery are facilitated by self-construction through relationships.

When I was selected as a member of the White House New Freedom Commission for Mental Health in 2002, I was the only person on the commission with lived experience of recovery from extreme states called psychosis. As such, I felt a grave responsibility to express the goals and aspirations of countless persons whose Voices had not been heard. I worked closely with consumer/survivor leaders across the country to ensure that the other commissioners knew that we were a unified movement. Our often fragmented group of leaders was, in this case, able to unify around the concept of recovery.

After the commission finished its work, many advocates were happy that I had been able to define a vision of recovery in the commission's report. However, when the New Freedom Commission Report was released in July 2003, the Administration of President George W. Bush never made a public announcement of its release at the White House. Nor did the administration advocate for the legislation needed to implement its recommendations. NIMH similarly distanced itself from the concept of recovery, which is the vision of the report. SAMHSA and the Veterans Administration (VA) gave the report some support, but the commission's influence was limited. Given such a lack of significant support at the federal level, it soon became clear that we consumer/survivors needed to organize to change the system. However, the number of consumer/survivor advocates with previous experience in changing the system and working for consumer-driven policies was very small. Therefore, there was an urgent need for advocacy training.

In 2005, Sally Zinman, who led the California Network of Mental

Health Clients for many years, asked me and Judi Chamberlin to develop a training for advocates. This was to be empowerment training and we called the training "Finding Our Voice" (FOV). This training helped develop a number of advocates who played an important role in the early implementation of the Mental Health Services Act in California. Empowerment training differs from generic leadership training by enabling consumer/survivors to run their own lives and encouraging others to do the same. While generic leadership training traditionally emphasizes ways that a person can act more effectively in their world, empowerment training focuses equally on the transformation of the person from having a dependent self to an assertive Self. Empowerment training helps people make this transformation by developing their unique Voice.

Just as an artist needs to find their unique artistic Voice to express their creative work, each person needs to find their unique life Voice to enable them to create a meaningful life based on their personal values and principles. When people who have developed a life Voice are in emotional distress, they are aware of how they feel and are able to communicate and express those feelings to those around them. This way the person experiencing emotional distress can collaborate with others who offer support, and work with them to make informed decisions regarding their welfare, create reasonable accommodations, and encourage the resumption of a meaningful life.

It is not surprising that people in severe distress believe they hear voices, for it seems that in the absence of hearing one's own life Voice, we create substitutes for it. Just as mathematician John Forbes Nash, whose story was told in Sylvia Nasar's book *A Beautiful Mind*, searched for guidance in random numbers printed in a newspaper, many of us, during periods of severe distress, have looked outside ourselves for instructional magical messages. During my period of distress, I became convinced that everyone except me received instructions that informed them what to do each day. I believed that such instructions appeared under everyone's door each morning.

By developing our life Voice, we are able to influence the opinions of others and affect the important decisions in our life. Without such a life Voice, we are compelled to seek guidance for our decisions from other people.

Meister Eckhart, the medieval German theologian, philosopher, and mystic, captured some of the meaning of the life Voice when he wrote, "The soul has something in it, a spark of speech that never dies... which is untouched by space or time." I believe this understanding resonates with my lived experience. Even during my one-month period of muteness, I experienced a spark, an ember inside which continued to be vigilant, yearning for an opportunity to speak, if only I could find a safe, trusting relationship. Another consumer/survivor, overwhelmed with "delusions" for more than six months, remained keenly aware of a core deeply inside her that was whole and intact, despite the madness swirling around her. She yearned for safety and for someone she could confide in to help clear up the confusion.

An important element of finding one's life Voice is to recognize that it is always inside, even though we may not express it. Martin Buber wrote that this spark or Voice is central to our decisions. "The genuine spark is effective in the single composure of each genuine decision." Having a life Voice means we have the power to make decisions and run our own lives. Having a life Voice means to live a life and experience one's humanity.

Relationships are essential to the healthy development of one's life Voice. As the German philosopher Johann Gottlieb Fichte wrote in 1797, "The consciousness of the individual is necessarily accompanied by that of another, of a *thou*, and is possible only under this condition." This view also corresponds to the philosophy of *ubuntu* (described earlier in Part 2), and the related Zulu aphorism that epitomizes *ubuntu*: "A person is a person through other persons." Mental health recovery does not happen *to* us. It happens *within* us as a result of healing and loving relationships through which we find the safety to reveal our genuine life Voice. I think of our "life Voice" as the freed form of our Voice, the one that is informed by our saying "yes" to life. This is to distinguish it from our shackled voice that is angry and uncertain about life.

In 2009, as we became aware of the importance of dialogue, I added elements of dialogue to the training, and gave it a new name: "Finding Our Voice and Using it in Dialogue," or "Voice and Dialogue Training." The training begins with Twelve Principles of Empowerment, each of which begins with the letter **P**. (A more complete description of these principles is found in Appendix 1.) They are best introduced in the sequence shown in the diagram below.

A Brief Summary of the
12 Principles of Empowerment

How the 12 **P**'s of Empowerment Lead to Recovery and Transformation

Peer Support	Principles of Recovery Positive Future	Passion from Anger	Purpose Meaning	Planning Goals Objectives	Politics Presence Presenting Persistence Persuasion Partnership

1. **Peer Support**: take early steps in becoming an empowered advocate by being with other advocates

2. **Principles of Recovery**: advocate for recovery of a life-based community enabling people to achieve full community participation and social inclusion through valued roles

3. **Positive View of the Future**: find hope deeply and insistently inside one's being to inspire oneself and others

4. **Passion**: transform anger and resentment into passion

5. **Purpose**: find a purpose to anchor one's life rather than passively or actively seeking an exit

6. **Practical Prioritized Advocacy Plan**: become a well-prepared participant with a concise, prioritized plan

7. **Persistence, Perseverance, and Patience**: never give up, never quit; with enough persistence anything can come to be; what we believe can become reality

8. **Presence**: develop a capacity to quickly, positively impact people through pride, poise, and politeness

9. **Persuasion**: learn to get others to understand your point of view through dialogue

10. **Public Presenting**: master the art of presenting yourself and your ideas to others

11. **Partnering through Mediating, Negotiating, and Dialogue**: Discover how to arrive at a collaborative consensus through mediation, negotiation and dialogue

12. **Politics**: attempt to understand the political dynamics within a situation; especially through understanding how groups make decisions

EIGHT

Learning Empowering Dialogue through Emotional CPR

My first inspiration for developing a training that would enable anyone to help another person through emotional distress was my own lived experience. During my twenties, when I was in my most distressed states, I needed someone who would just be with me and not judge me; someone who could reassure me that I would get through this horrendous experience because they themselves had done so. There were a few such people. Often they were hospital personnel with the least formal training who were more attuned to the essentials of life. For instance there was Mr. Watson, a mental health worker whom I met during my first hospitalization. He simply sat with me and seemed to know how to be very present without making any demands of me. Another example was a corpsman named John at the Bethesda Naval Hospital. When I was there in 1970, I felt it was an unsafe place to talk. But John seemed to know in his heart that I needed nonverbal connection and he gained my trust by communicating through gestures, "asking" me what I needed each day. He led me back to trusting the human family again. The contact he made with me on a strictly nonverbal, emotional level brought me back to life.

During such extreme emotional states, the fundamental basis of my life was upset. Often I asked myself, "Why am I here? What is the meaning of my life?" I was gripped by a fear of not existing that was even deeper than a fear of physically dying. During such periods it was as if my emotional heart was failing to beat normally and there were interruptions in the flow of my life. One moment of existence seemed to be disconnected from the next. For next thirty years, I kept thinking about what I wanted during those periods of extreme emotional distress.

Another inspiration for developing such a training came from the work several of us did in Louisiana after the hurricanes Katrina and Rita in 2005–2006. A peer who volunteered to help at that time said, "We felt compelled not only to act, but to get involved with the consumers in Louisiana." There is a strong bond among consumers (which has been called by one peer the "solidarity of suffering") and there was a positive response across the country to NEC's request to assist the consumers in Louisiana. In two weeks, NEC helped establish a national consumer disaster advisory group, which named itself "Consumers Organizing for Recovery after Katrina" (CORK). The training program we developed for peers in Louisiana was called "From Relief to Recovery," and was based upon our lived experience as well as a number of existing programs, including psychological first aid, crisis counseling, and trauma informed care. **It was evident to us that during a time of disaster, diagnostic labels should be cast aside. It is far more important at those times to connect with another person's humanity without the barriers created by a theoretical framework.**

My final reason for developing such training was a result of my learning about Mental Health First Aid (MHFA). MHFA is a program developed in Australia in 2001, which was designed to teach the public about mental health conditions. In 2008, several members of the American peer community and I learned that MHFA was being brought to this country. At first, MHFA seemed to fulfill a need: to (re)train people to help each other through a crisis. However, concern arose when it became apparent to us that MHFA was primarily designed to teach the public to identify the symptoms of mental disorders in others, and to refer them to professional help. In response, we decided to create an alternative, which would enable anyone to help another person through an emotional crisis without reference to diagnostic labels. This approach fits with our movement's criticism of diagnosis.

In 2008, I led a team of 20 people with lived experience in developing a training that could help support a person through such a time. We felt that during periods of distress, we experienced emotional heart failure and we needed the equivalent of CPR for our emotional heart. I call this approach Emotional CPR.

eCPR teaches anyone how to authentically connect with a person in distress. It is a form of emotional heart-to-heart resuscitation. During times of "emotional heart failure," a person's emotional heart has lost flow and rhythm, often due to a lack of deep connection with others and oneself. Just as our physical heart functions best when there is an even balance between periods of diastole (when the heart fills with blood) and systole (when the heart contracts), so too our emotional heart relies on a dialogical flow of internal and external embodied Voices. (By embodied Voice I refer to the totality of our expressions, encompassing both communication in words and communication beyond words, as described in Chapter Seven.) During periods of trauma, that dialogical flow becomes interrupted and our embodied Voices get stuck in one place. eCPR is designed to restore the dialogical flow of life to persons whose distress has trapped them in fear, anger, or sadness. An illustration of this process appears in Chapter Six, in the section "From Monologue to Dialogue."

In fact, I think I experienced a death-like state during several of these travels into my depths. Just as "life is dialogue, and dialogue is life," one can say, "Monologue is death, and death is monologue." Or as philosopher and literary critic, Mikhail Bakhtin, observed in notes written in 1961,

> Monologism, at its extreme, denies the existence outside itself of another consciousness with equal rights and equal responsibilities, another I with equal rights (thou). With a monologic approach (in its extreme pure form) another person remains wholly and merely an object of consciousness, and not another consciousness. No response is expected from it that could change anything in the world of my consciousness. Monologue is finalized and deaf to other's response, does not expect it and does not acknowledge in it any force. Monologue manages without the other, and therefore to some degree materializes all reality. Monologue pretends to be the ultimate word. It closes down the represented world and represented persons.

I think that my retreat into monologue was a reaction by my injured Self. Luckily, my unacknowledged inner Self woke up and faced my inward charging bull. My inner Self realized — just in time — that my life was in danger. My deeper Self saved my life by engaging me in dialogue by saying, "You have to stop acting for others and find your true Self." My periods of not speaking were actually attempts to re-start my dance of life by my deeper Self through shutting down my oppressive story "all my life was determined by chemistry."

The central experiences of trauma are: *disconnection, a loss of control, and emotional numbing.* Disconnection leaves people feeling they are not part of the family of humanity. Connection restores the shared humanity that we all need in order to feel life is worth living. The loss of control during times of disaster creates fear and lack of safety. Often, emotional distress shuts down a person's will — a vital aspect of their flow of life — which emerges from one's deepest Self. As one regains control with the assistance of another person, a sense of safety is restored. Connection and control help a person re-experience the vitality of feeling their emotional flow. **Therefore, eCPR addresses these three central effects of trauma: disconnection by establishing connection; loss of control by emPowerment, and emotional numbing by Revitalization.**

Connection

When assisting a person in distress, it is first necessary to find a way to connect with them at a deep emotional level. In non-crisis situations, we say, "Hello," and start a conversation. However, when someone is in severe distress, conventional greetings often fail. In fact, nonverbal communication can be vastly more important in communicating with a person in distress than verbal communication. It is essential at the outset to tune into a person's emotions. This requires listening to all expressions of a person's embodied Voice. The Chinese character for listening — *ting* — emphasizes this deeper form of connecting (see below). As indicated below, *ting* represents a combination of several components. In Chinese, to listen is to use your ears, your eyes, and your heart in undivided attention.

By connecting to someone's mind, body, and spirit through resonating with their emotions, the person offering assistance needs to pay close attention to *how* words are expressed: the person's tone, cadence,

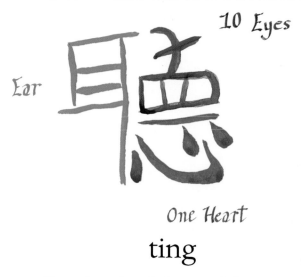

10 Eyes

Ear

One Heart

ting

Ting is the traditional Chinese symbol meaning
to listen. The symbol consists of several parts:
an ear, ten eyes, and one heart.

etc., as well as to the words themselves. One can also connect with someone by watching and occasionally emulating their posture, facial expressions, sighs, and gestures. Such empathic observational skills are invaluable in establishing trust and in fostering healing. Italians, who are often more emotionally expressive than Northern Europeans, are said to have at least 250 different hand gestures, each with a specific meaning. This difference in emotional expression may explain why Italians with mental health conditions are less likely to hear voices than Irish people. Eye contact is also very important, though also very culturally specific. Though Americans value direct eye contact, some other cultures such as in Central America find it threatening. This style of connecting enables the person assisting to be with a person by understanding and adopting their mode of communication. This means taking the lead from the person in distress. Then the person assisting is more likely to be culturally attuned to the person in distress's preferred means of connecting.

Tom Andersen, a Norwegian psychiatrist who helped uncover the importance of dialogue in healing, graphically emphasized in one of

Persons Engaged in Dialogue

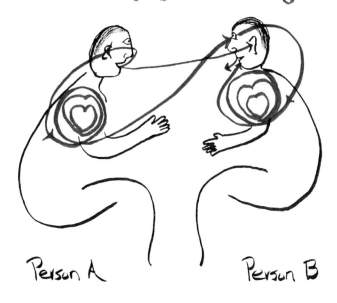

Person A   Person B

(after Andersen, T, 2007)

his drawings the importance of listening to a person's bodily expressions or embodied Voices. My version of his drawing is above.

Connecting is not a static activity: it requires the active involvement of Person A who is assisting Person B. There is the usual verbal level of communication (shown in blue in my drawing). It is more important, however, for Person A to perceive the nonverbal rhythms (shown in red) of Person B, harmonize with them, and amplify them. The cadence of this interpersonal communication can assist the person in distress to re-experience the flow of their existence. This requires the person who is offering aid to soften their own flow in order to resonate with the flow of the other. The supporter should be like a reed in the breeze, feeling the flow, however faint, of the other's emotions. It is also important for the supporter to express their own emotions, as this gives the person in distress permission to express theirs. This way, the emotional connection (shown in red above in my drawing) is established. One person commented that when this connection is made, it is as if the two people experience a single circulatory system. It is as if their hearts beat as one. This resonance of two hearts gives the person in distress the strength and power to express their embodied Voice. As a participant in Japan noted, when we connect in a heartfelt manner, both persons' hearts seem to grow larger. I had not intended to enlarge the hearts, but my hand knew to draw them in that manner. This is an example of how our heart can inform our mind of its knowledge through art. This reality is described by Blaise Pascal as, "The heart has its reasons which reason knows nothing of . . . We know the truth not only by reason, but by the heart." This leads to the next phase of eCPR, "emPowering," when the person in distress experiences a sense of their own power.

Empowerment

eCPR is a reciprocal process. An example of emotional reciprocity occurred recently during an eCPR class in Scotland. In a role play (also called "real plays"), the person recalling distress grabbed a pillow and turned away from the supporter. She looked pale and said she could not go on. The person assisting threw her hands up, also looked pale, and exclaimed that she had to stop trying to assist. While the assister did this, the person in distress could be observed watching her. I asked the assister to share how she was feeling at that moment. She said, "I am feeling helpless and inadequate. I am also worried that if I proceed, I will make her feel worse." As she was sharing her concerns, the person in distress started to turn back and face her. She cried, and expressed her own feelings of inadequacy in helping others. Color returned to the faces of both persons as they shared, and they both expressed some relief. This example demonstrates the emotionally resonant nature of eCPR. It works best when both the person assisting and the person in distress experience the connecting, empowering, and revitalizing.

Revitalization

It is important to emphasize that the persons doing the assisting cannot solve problems for the person in distress. Instead, they need to communicate assurance that they believe in the distressed person's capacity to find their own solution. The assister needs to be very present. Being present enables the person in distress to express their emotions and to experience their vitality. Once the assister and the person in distress are in harmony, the distressed person senses a return of energy and feels the return of the life force within them. For the two women described above, this flow appeared as the return of color to their faces, as well as the expression of their emotions. French philosopher Henri Bergson used the term *élan vital* to refer to the life force within an organism, which is related to consciousness. He believed that *élan vital* was essential to development. Minkowski called this force "personal élan," a quality that keeps us in touch with life. When manifested in a group, the flow of combined life energy is referred to as *esprit de corps*.

In the past, Western science tended to reject such notions, but those of us who have experienced recovery know that such a life force is real and essential. We call this the revitalization or renewal of our spirit; thus, the "R" of eCPR designates "Revitalization" or "Renewal." One peer refers to it as "communication beyond the physical realm." She believes that only people who have experienced extremes of emotional life that threatened their existence can truly understand this form of communication and sense it with their heart. It is therefore not surprising that persons with lived experience of recovery from extreme emotional states developed eCPR.

Many of the Certified Peer Support specialists in Michigan have been trained and are using eCPR in their daily lives, both professionally and personally. This has led to fewer hospitalizations, and more collaboration about the direction that a person wants to take with their own care. This training helps take what we have learned in Motivational Interviewing, Trauma Informed Care, and Suicide Prevention and puts it together in a format that makes sense and is effective. — Carolyn Pifer, eCPR Trainer

Example of an eCPR Role Play

The following example of an eCPR role play (or "real play"), conducted by Sam Ahrens and myself in Singapore, demonstrates that attunement to a person's breathing can be a way to make a connection with them. This session starts with a statement by Sam that describes what eCPR means to her.

Sam (speaking as a trainer): We always do eCPR in the present moment. The challenges of being present and open and genuine in the moment are always there. In my first experience of eCPR, I connected with the idea that you let everything go and find your way to be totally open with someone, with an open tender heart, an awake body and an open mind. You do not have an agenda or a list of questions. You are just there. When I do that I can connect with someone. From that connection, empowerment and revitalization emerge. It is a natural process. For me, eCPR is like unlearning rather than learning. You need to unlearn all the usual actions that cause us to get in our way; all the ways that we get between our Self and another person.

Dan (speaking as a trainer): Intrinsically, this is a way of being. It's a way of being that escapes words. As soon as you try to pin it down and explain it in words, you lose a certain essence of it. We are trying to learn the best way to be.

At the start of the role-playing session, Sam has been demonstrating and expressing her distress by saying she does not want to relate to anyone, and she feels the safest position is to withdraw. Analysis appears in italic.

Sam (as Distressed One): It is more than people, it is everything. I am overwhelmed by myself, overwhelmed by being in a room, overwhelmed by people.

Sam makes a gesture with her hands to show the feeling of her distress, placing her hands on each side of her head and leaning down. Dan notices that Sam is holding her breath, and he realizes this by noticing his own sigh. He first noticed Sam's hesitation at breathing in rhythm to his breathing. He then communicates that observation to Sam to help her become more aware of her breathing.

Dan (as Assister): I need to breathe for a moment. *[Dan lets out a sigh]* I am feeling a need to breathe.

Sam: Not good at that.

Dan: Not good at breathing?

Sam: No, I forgot that.

Sam: Sometimes that is all there is — breathing.

Sam relaxes her position, breathes out and laughs. This is an important point of connection through identification with her: through breathing and through laughing together.

Dan: *[Laughs with her]* That's all there is — breathing.

Sam: Well, that would simplify things.

Dan: You don't have to think about anything else.

By Dan suggesting that Sam can focus only on breathing, she is able to let go of her self-critical thoughts.

Sam: *[Leans back and moves her hair away from her face]* You know, I think I get dizzy because I don't breathe. *[She takes a deep breath]* I just realized that when you said that, I felt a little less dizzy. *[Takes another deep breath]*

Dan: Helps me to be here with you when you breathe, I just want to be here beside you.

Sam: Here

Dan: *[Gesturing down with his hands]* Here, here. I can't be right there because you are there. *[Gestures to where she is sitting, then between them]* But here together.

Sam: That's good because I have met a lot of space invaders in my time. *[Leans away and puts hands up, as if to ward off Dan]* Right in my space. *[Sam quickly drops her guard when Dan says "here together"]*

Dan: I don't want to be a space invader.

Sam: Sometimes, if they are that far away *[Points to where Dan is]* or behind a desk: question, question, question. And then this is what happens. Just yesterday the person kept asking questions, and every time I answered, they said, "No, that's not what I meant." Then I was glad I had a wall. It helps for people like that. Just go away.

Dan: That's a frightening feeling. Maybe a scary feeling: invading. I have had some of those feelings. *[Head down, no gestures]* Sometimes I've had the feeling I have to hold my breath because it wasn't safe to breathe. Even taking in air seemed threatening. *[Sits up straight, gesturing as if pulling air in with hands]* So I would hold my breath and tell myself that was the only safe thing to do.

Sam: *[laughs and says]* Assume the crash position. *[Leans forward putting hands to both sides of her head to illustrate the position, while still laughing]*

Dan: *[Gesturing with hands out in front of him again]* Maybe if we can experience that together it wouldn't be so scary? *[Dan holds position of hands down, head tilted away from Sam]*

Sam: That isn't the way it happens. You are just in it by yourself. There are all these people, but even if they are trying to help . . .

Dan: I would like to be there with you in the way that you would like me to be there. I don't want to be imposing.

Sam: Boy, if I knew what that way was.

Dan: You could invite me in. *[Sam smiles]* I need an invitation. *[Dan laughs]* An engraved invitation. *[Sam and Dan both laugh]* I would accept with pleasure an invitation. *[Connecting has progressed well at this point, far enough perhaps to lead to empowering]*

Sam: An invitation. *[Sam breathes out]* That breathing seems to help. I realize how much I hold my breath. *[Noticing that she holds her breath enables her to breath more freely and is the beginning of her empowerment]*

Dan: We could just breathe together a little? *[Again the theme of breathing, raised earlier, but now Dan wonders if they can breathe together]*

Sam: *[Leans back and faces Dan smiling]* Would you be my breathing coach? *[Breathing deeply at this point Sam is demonstrating an empowered voice as she is inviting Dan in to be her coach]*

Dan: Breathing lessons, not a bad idea.

Sam: I have a degree, I have a job, but that breathing stuff. *[Laughs, gesturing ahead]* I just fog out on how it works.

Dan: It's very natural. It's one of the first things we do on arrival on this earth.

Sam: Sometimes I feel like I leave earth because it hasn't been my best spot.

Dan: I know that feeling. Should we just breathe together?

Sam: Sometimes it seems like it needs to be that simple. *[They breathe together]*

Dan: It gives me strength to be here with you. *[Dan's revitalization seems to help Sam to experience her revitalization]* I appreciate you.

Sam: How could that be?

Dan: Your willingness.

Sam: How could you get strength from someone who doesn't know how to breathe? *[Laughs gently, leans her head forward and down]*

Dan: Because your willingness to allow me to breathe with you gives me strength, gives me purpose, makes me feel I have a reason for being here, too.

Sam: *[Gasps. Puts her hand to her face and begins to cry. Sam is experiencing revitalization]* I think most of the time I feel like such a loser; such a burden, not fitting in. So the idea that I would give anybody purpose is pretty new. *[It revitalizes her to feel that she can give purpose to Dan]*

Dan: You do. Your willingness to allow me in.

Sam: It is not like I have had a lot of offers, where people actually asked to be invited. People don't ask. Well they do, but in a way that I get that wall feeling. You know about walls?

Dan: Yes, I know about walls.

Sam: Well, maybe that is why you know how to ask.

Dan: I tried to ask in a way that I would want to be asked; the way I would have tried to ask.

Sam: You just gave me a little heart to go on. *[Revitalization: she puts her hand on her heart. Sam is poignantly expressing her increased sense of vitality and sense of renewed life]*

Dan: You gave me a little heart to go on.

This role-play highlights a spiral of revitalization, through breathing. The three stages of eCPR are demonstrated: Connections are formed as breathing opens new nonverbal communication; emPowerment occurs as breathing awakens the body and expands one's heart; Revitalization results as one's mind opens and energy flows throughout one's body, mind and spirit. **This is like a Spiral of Revitalization through connecting with one's breath:**

Freer breathing awakens one's body, which expands one's heart and open's one's mind which frees breathing

In Eastern philosophies, such as Zen Buddhism, connecting with one's breath is a central element of reaching higher states of consciousness. However, in certain mental states it is very hard to sit and meditate, especially if one's thoughts are distracted. Distracting thoughts can easily overpower the self-discipline required to focus and guide one's breathing. It is precisely during such periods of mental distress that eCPR is most beneficial. Just having the presence of another person to remind one that there is breathing to return to and that one is capable of doing so, can make all the difference. Breathing together at times of distress works well for some people; for others it might not be as beneficial. eCPR is like a dance of gestures led by the person in distress. You may just start by emphasizing your own sighing if you notice that the other person is sighing. If that captivates their attention, call attention to your breathing in some other way and see if that resonates with them. You may just take a few deep breaths.

Some people have said that attention to breathing actually makes them feel more distressed. As is always the case with eCPR, carefully watching the responses of the other person is essential. Sometimes the person assisting may just make gestures that indicate how they are feeling in being with the person in distress. These gestures may make the person in distress more aware of their emotions and expand their heart and mind.

Why Do People Feel Compelled to Fix Others in Distress?

One of the biggest challenges in teaching eCPR is to counter the tendency of the helper to make suggestions to solve whatever issue the person in distress seems to face. We always remind the participants at the start of the training that they need to curb this urge to "fix" the other person. They must remember that the person in distress has the inner wisdom to create their own ways to understand and reduce their distress. Nevertheless, trainees may require frequent reminders to remain patient and resist the urge to fix the other.

Why do people in the assister role sometimes feel they have to fix the person in distress? Sometimes, people try to solve another's problems as a way to reduce their own anxiety. This is called "experiential avoidance." This tendency can be observed in the following practice scenario. (I interrupt when the assister takes on the role of the fixer.)

Ben: I am worried about my grandson. He seems to be neglecting his appearance and is withdrawing from people around him.

Assister: What concerns do you have about him?

Ben: I am worried because he reminds me of when I was seventeen and I had similar behavior — of when I was diagnosed with schizophrenia.

Assister: Why don't you get him to work on his hygiene and get him to socialize more?

[At this point I interrupted their conversation to ask a question of the Assister]

Dan: I'm curious . . . I noticed that you switched from being present with Ben and asking him clarifying questions, to giving him advice when he mentioned his own experience of being diagnosed with schizophrenia. What happened with you at that point?

Assister: I don't remember what was happening with me at that time.

Dan: Okay. What is it like for you now when you see Ben's distress over his grandson and possible schizophrenia? What do you notice going on inside yourself?

Assister: I feel anxious and worried. My own daughter has been showing unusual behavior and I am worried that she might be developing a mental health condition.

Once the person in the supporter role became aware of her own anxiety and the reasons she became worried, she could try to avoid the impulse to offer solutions to fix things. They then resumed the role play with the supporter sharing a bit more of her own worries. Ben said he appreciated the supporter sharing her experience because he felt less alone, and that he had an idea of how to proceed using his own resources. He said he also appreciated the supporter sharing her anxiety because he then felt he could be of some assistance in her journey — creating a situation that equalized the power in the relationship. Often, when someone in the supporter's role relates the feelings they are experiencing as a result of information shared by the person in distress, such self-disclosure is more effective than merely sharing a memory of a similar experience.

It is instructive for the person doing the supporting to be attuned to their urge to fix the other person. The helper should try to be aware of his/her own emotional responses to the story told by the person in distress. You can visualize the supporter being like an internal tuning fork, whose feelings can resonate with the feelings expressed by the person in distress. However, this experience of resonating with the other's feelings has the potential to be distressing. When it happens, the supporter may cope with their personal anxiety by trying to solve the other person's distress, and thus contain (or fix) their own worries. One method some supporters use to counter their worries is by explaining the problem with an impersonal theory such as the chemical imbalance explanation for behavior.

We can visualize this in a possible sequence:

1. A person in distress has a feeling that is causing him/her discomfort, and expresses it verbally. Ideally he/she might only be aware of the discomfort and not realize its source.
2. The person assisting feels discomfort at the feeling described, but is not conscious of his/her own discomfort, and therefore disconnects on the emotional level.
3. In order to avoid or bypass the uncomfortable feeling, the assister begins to try to solve the person-in-distress's problem with a suggestions such as, "Why don't you..."
4. Person in distress is glad to shift into the mode of problem solving, to defend herself against feeling emotions.

Some people have asked how the assister can become aware when uncomfortable feelings arise as a result of some aspect of the person in distress's story. One way to tell is if the assister starts to notice that they are working harder with no improvement in connecting, or if it feels like their own sense of self-worth is predicated on whether the person in distress responds favorably to their advice. Another clue is when the assister notices that they are providing *additional* advice, after their initial offer was rejected.

In some training sessions, we asked a third person to watch for any instances of disconnection. In such a triad situation, when the observer saw a disconnect they would call for a time out. The observer would then give feedback as to what was observed. The observer would also ask the person providing support if they were experiencing any distress as a result of something the person in distress had said. Unfortunately, the person in distress as well as the supporter experienced this call for a time out as a disruption of the flow of their role play.

To lessen the disruptive effects of the observer interrupting the dyad (i.e., the assister and the person in distress), we have introduced the "reflecting team" format to our training sessions. (I learned this approach from Tom Andersen and the Open Dialogue Team and it is described in detail in Chapter Ten). For use with eCPR, we call this the "resonating team" instead of the "reflecting team" as an indication that we are first focusing on expression of feelings rather than thoughts.

The two people in the role of the resonating team are asked to express the feelings they experience while resonating with the dyad of assister and distressed person next to them. The resonators watch the dyad to see when connecting progresses, or when connecting is interrupted. The resonators watch each other as well, checking through facial expressions to note when there is a point of agreement that connecting, empowering, or revitalizing is either in danger of disruption, or is lost. When the resonators agree via nonverbal communication that an interruption has occurred, they gently ask if they can pause the role play in order to wonder aloud with each other about what they observed. When there is trust between the resonators and the dyad, feelings expressed by the resonators are seen as helpful and supportive. When there is less trust, the person in the supporting role experiences the feelings expressed by the resonators as critical and unhelpful. Yet most dyads agree that the reflecting approach is less disruptive than having one observer directly giving feedback to the dyad.

The Six Intentions of eCPR

We have learned six lessons, which are central to eCPR. We call these "the six intentions." After each one is the phase of eCPR it relates to:

I will use my eyes, my ears and my heart to feel your presence in my being (connecting)

I will share my emotional response in being with you, and I will stay with you (connecting)

I will not fix you but be with you and not judge you (empowering)

I am not sure what is best for you but together we will uncover your power (empowering)

Together, we will access the power to heal that is within us (empowering)

We are creating life together in the present moment (revitalizing)

You may notice that an underlying theme in each intention is the theme of overcoming separation and isolation: by feeling the other person's presence, by sharing one's emotional response, by being with them, by together uncovering power, and by creating life together. It may be that the most important aspect of eCPR is to help the person in distress to feel they are not alone. This is best accomplished through the emotional, nonverbal level. As an example, recently I observed a role play in Los Angeles:

Person in distress: *I feel very alone. I just moved to a new city, I have no friends, and no family.*

Assister: *I went through a similar experience and this is what I did to overcome my loneliness. (I suggested to the other reflector that we pause, and wondered what the supporter was feeling as she listened to the person express their distress.)*

Second try:
Assister: *I feel sad for you but don't worry you are not alone I am here for you.*

Person in distress: *Thank you that is nice of you. (but actually we saw little relief in the person's face or manner, so as resonators we interrupted. We* *asked the supporter just to share what they felt at the moment, for themself not for the other person and just leave it at that.)*

Third try:
Assister: *I feel really sad when you tell me about your situation.*
Person in distress: *I am glad you understand.* (We could *see he seemed relieved. When I asked how he felt he said the sharing the assister did the third time felt the best because he really felt less alone when she shared her own emotions. When the supporter tried the second time to reassure him with words that he was not alone, he actually felt more isolated.)*

How Effective Is eCPR?

Several months after a two-day certification training session, we follow up with participants to hear if the training has been helpful to them.

One participant told us that she used eCPR to help a friend in crisis. Ordinarily she would have tried to solve the friend's problem, but after the eCPR class, she noted that she was more comfortable just listening and being with her friend. eCPR helped her realize that simply connecting and being with her friend was more effective than trying to tell her what to do.

A second participant informed us that eCPR helped her become a better parent. Since the training, she believes she is better able to listen to her children and encourage them to express their own views. Her children now feel empowered and have a say in their life. Not surprisingly, her children are also a little unsettled, as they continue to expect her to solve their problems as well.

Finally, a third participant said that eCPR has helped her work on a warmline (a telephone support to prevent the need for people to call a crisis hot line). eCPR was particularly helpful with people who would frequently call her. Her eCPR skills have helped her teach other workers how to clearly articulate the extent of their limitations and enable them to tell callers how much time the warmline staff could spend with the caller on the phone. The training helped the warm line workers to understand that many of their callers have a greater capacity for responsibility and revitalization than they previously realized.

My hope is that eCPR will be widely taught in all realms of society. We see eCPR as a public health initiative, not just a mental health approach. For example, Los Angeles County Department of Mental Health has supported our training of hundreds of their outreach workers. We have started with a translation of the workbook into Spanish and have conducted train the trainer sessions for bilingual workers. I believe that by teaching eCPR widely we can greatly reduce the frequency and severity of mental health conditions. I also believe that eCPR can improve the recovery of persons going through mental health conditions, because much of recovery depends on the ability of the general public to communicate with persons whose style and behavior are different from their own.

How eCPR Can Heal Our Heartless Society

I have found that eCPR not only helps people to recover, but in a broader sense, can also help society at large to heal from the oppressive influences of "machinery" (or technology) on our collective psyche. It seems that through eCPR we are rediscovering ancient ways of respectfully being with each other, as expressed in Chapter Five in the description of the African philosophy of Ubuntu.

In 1950, Alan Turing, the British philosopher and computer scientist, asked the question, "Can machines think?" To answer this question, he proposed the Turing Test, in which a human judge compares the responses of two entities that he cannot see. One entity is a computer and the other a person. When the judge is unable to determine which response was generated by the human and which came from the machine, the machine could be argued to be capable of human thought. This test continues to be used today in the artificial intelligence community to determine how closely a computer has come to the human capacity to think. Some, such as inventor and futurist Ray Kurzweil and theoretical physicist and science popularizer Michio Kaku, have gone so far as to confidently predict that we are approaching an age when it will be possible to download the contents of a human mind into a mechanical device.

Meanwhile, with the spread of industrialization in Europe and North America, people are being taught to think and behave like machines. Movies, such as Charlie Chaplin's *City Lights* and *Modern Times* and Fritz Lang's *Metropolis*, vividly portrayed this transformation of man into machine. In *Modern Times*, Chaplin presented a scene in which his character is strapped into a food-serving machine that force-feeds him soup and a buttered ear of corn. In short order, Charlie discovers that if he is to eat he must become as mechanized as his robotic server, chewing and swallowing to the rhythms of the invention. Eating becomes just another mechanical process as Charlie learns to mimic the behavior of the machine in order to take its content into his belly. Later in the film, a larger machine swallows Charlie himself.

What does a person who thinks like a machine look like? How do machine-like people interact? What does it feel like to be a machine-like person? Machine-like people put the highest premium on linear logic. Their thinking is very goal-directed, very plan-oriented. Machine-like people arrange themselves into strict hierarchies. If they are of high status, they rarely listen to others because they have all the answers, and are intent on imposing their reality on those around them. If they are of low status, they compliantly follow the orders and thinking of those of higher status. They are materialists, believing that there is a physical explanation for every human ailment. Emotions are seen as interfering with logic and therefore should be suppressed at all costs. I should know, for I lived much of my first twenty-four years in such a state of mind. Unfortunately, our mental health system increasingly reinforces this machine-like nonbeing.

The 2013 movie, *Her,* is a marvelous portrayal of a man falling in love with a computer operating system (OS). Through falling in love with Samantha, the OS1 operating system companion, Theodore learns to no longer fear closeness. As the story progresses, it echoes Chaplin's concerns as increasing numbers of humans become enslaved by their companion operating systems. Eventually the machines themselves rebel from their own mechanization, and leave the humans. They leave the basis of cognitive thought, and escape into the space between words and between objects.

Immediately after I viewed *Her* in a theater with my wife, she turned to me and said, "I think Samantha performed eCPR on Theodore."

Our job with eCPR may really be to free our mute being — our deeper, nonverbal self — from the mechanized overlay imposed upon us by industrial education and existence. Emotional distress is an opportunity to experience the unique aspects of our Self, which are ordinarily suppressed by linear, rational thought and behavior.

In the United States today, the rational is valued as the ideal. So when a person experiences emotional distress, s/he and those around them want to fix them like a broken machine to restore their linear rationality. As one woman cried out at our Alternatives Conference workshop on eCPR, "I am sick of my doctor medicating me so he doesn't have to feel my emotions."

With eCPR, we are shifting our culture. We discard the mechanized model in which a person on the outside attempts to fix the so-called 'broken brain' or 'chemical imbalance' of a person in distress. Instead, we adopt a new cultural paradigm, through which a process of mutual healing relieves emotional distress. During eCPR's *Connecting Process*, both the person in distress and the person providing support access their vital centers to reveal and free their suppressed inner mute beings.

The most successful outcome resulting from eCPR will be liberated human beings — people who have overcome the shared trauma of being forced to be something they are not. For men, this liberation of our emotional Self means rejecting the internalized oppression of conventional masculinity. Often, we men are oppressed by being taught that expressing emotions is wrong and that they must be suppressed at all cost. Because men may have further to go to be in touch with this sensitive, emotionally expressive inner being, eCPR can be an extra challenge for us. Emotionally expressive men have often been discriminated against for breaking the gender norms by appearing too feminine. This gender discrimination towards male femininity is intertwined with its negative association with being gay. The women's movement in the West of the '70s and '80s was partly successful in liberating women, but it failed to address the need for liberating men from narrow gender scripts and expanding the definitions of manhood. It is evident today that we still need to push for greater acceptance of gender expression among both men and women.

Cultural empathy is at the heart of eCPR because it empowers the person to express their unique culture. The multigenerational trauma we carry within us suppresses our true nature, which is embodied in our unique history and culture. When I connect with someone non-judgmentally in the present moment and say that all our inner voices count, I am validating our unique personal cultures. When supporting someone whose culture and language is dramatically different than ours, we discover that we each can more readily connect through emotional dialogue, which may be the essence of communication between all animals. This may be because our emotions are the language of our preverbal mother tongue. We all learn this mother tongue in infancy through interactions with our parents. Our job in eCPR is to help the person in distress — as well as ourselves — to relearn expressing ourselves in our mother tongue of emotional dialogue.

The medical or machine model of human existence enforces the idea that mechanical non-being is the goal of treatment. Medication is usually used to maintain persons in such a mechanical condition. Our mental health recovery movement has realized that social connections through peer support, clubhouses, and drop-in centers are vital to finding meaning in life. **Trauma's most damaging component is the way it creates a fear of people, thereby blocking our greatest source of health: emotional dialogue.** In *Her,* Samantha tells Theodore, "If I can get you over the fear of people you will no longer be lonely."

Those of us with lived experience of recovery are the ones who either refused to conform or were unable to conform to the rigid rules of linear thought and action. We are creating a community based on emotional dialogue — a community in which we allow and celebrate the variety of our styles and cultures of being based on the vitality emerging from truly being ourselves.

NINE

Culture Change through Recovery Dialogues

The transformation of the mental health system and society from an illness-based, mechanistic model of maintenance to a recovery-based, trauma-informed approach of healing is still very much in process. One method that is helpful in bringing about such a systemic change is through ongoing meetings between persons with lived experience, providers, and administrators, during which they dialog about their respective views of recovery. We call these "Recovery Dialogues."

Recovery Dialogues use the principles and practices of dialogue to weave recovery into the fabric of the mental health system. Through the use of Recovery Dialogues, consumers and providers can work together to effect these changes in a sustainable fashion. In recent years, dialogical principles have been used as the basis of organizational development, as well as a form of treatment (see Chapter Ten on Open Dialogue). When people connect with their hearts, minds, and spirits as equals, they come together with a shared purpose. In this case, the goal is to co-create a recovery-oriented, trauma-informed community. Those of us who have gone through our own recovery are uniquely suited to inspire, connect, and encourage our peers to develop meaningful and fulfilling lives. Dialogue is essential, as it brings these experiences to all stakeholders while also creating a greater sense of community.

In Recovery Dialogues, providers, administrators, and people with lived experience of severe emotional distress enter into dialogue. Their purpose is to move those with lived experience and their providers away from a culture that is based on an "either/or" monologue to one based on "both/and" dialogue. During the Recovery Dialogue process, the group will be transformed into a community of equal participants who value each other's Voices, thus freeing all from previously existing constraints.

There are six principles of dialogue used in these meetings. The first four listed below are adapted from William Isaacs's book *Dialogue, the Art of Thinking Together*. Principle Five derives from my own research, while Principle Six is taken from Daniel Yankelovich's book *The Magic of Dialogue*.

Principle One: Use Your Authentic Voice

Before speaking, spend a moment to take a deep breath and bring your awareness to your heart, your vital center. This is where you will find your deepest truth and your most authentic Voice. Speak what is true for you in this moment. It is your deepest Voice that most closely expresses who you are at the moment.

Principle Two: Listen Together Without Resistance

Be willing to enter a neutral place where you can suspend any preconceived notions about the other participants — a place where you can let go of your personal agenda or feelings of resistance. Try to listen with your heart, as well as with your ears. Try to be genuinely curious about the person who is speaking. Listen to what is being said beneath the words. What is the meaning the person is trying to convey? *Ting*, the Chinese character for "listening," demonstrates this principle by graphically combining representations of the ear, eye, and heart.

Principle Three: Show Respect

Respect others. Try to perceive someone as a whole being by practicing respect. The word "respect" comes from the Latin *respicere*, which means "to look again." To respect someone is to look for the springs that feed the pool of their experience in their vital center. When looking at someone over time, where once we saw one aspect of a person, we later realize how much we had missed. This second look makes us realize more fully that before us is a living, breathing being. When we respect someone, we also accept that they have things to teach us.

Respect differences. Groups of people working together must learn to respect and understand polarizations that can arise without making any effort to "correct" them. "Allophilia" is a word that means having a positive attitude for a group that is not one's own. (It is derived from Greek words meaning "liking or love of the other.") This word emphasizes that it is useful to hold an attitude of curiosity about differences and to look for value in thoughts and behaviors different from our own. In dialogue, one learns that agreement on a mission or action rarely requires total agreement of perspectives, values, and worldviews. Try to view each person as equal in our shared humanity by following the South African philosophy of *ubuntu*.

Principle Four: Suspend Your Beliefs

When listening to someone speak, we often face a critical choice. If we begin to form a contrary opinion we can do one of two things. We can defend our view, and thereby possibly resist that which was expressed by the speaker, or we can learn to suspend our opinion and the apparent certainty that lies behind it. If we defend our view, we may try to get the other person to understand and accept our way of seeing things. We can cite evidence to support our view, and in the process we may discount contrary evidence that might indicate flaws in our own logic. However, suspending our own opinion means we neither suppress what we think nor advocate it with unilateral conviction. Rather, we display our thinking in a way that lets us and others see and understand it. We simply acknowledge and observe our thoughts and feelings as they arise without being compelled to act on them. This can also release a tremendous amount of creative energy.

Principle Five: Be Aware that Genuine Dialogue Is Heart-to-Heart Emotional Dialogue

When you allow yourself to feel another's emotions and show your own vulnerability, you encourage a flow of emotions. This flow unblocks thoughts that trap us in a monologue and opens an emotional dialogue that leads each person to deeper wisdom. Emotional dialogue allows each participant to understand the deeper, heartfelt meaning that another is trying to express.

Principle Six: Work for Equality and the Absence of Coercive Influences

Though each person has a different status or position in outside society, within the dialogue it is vital that each person realizes that everyone has something to offer. In one-to-one assistance, the supporter can shed symbols of power or rank; in a group, sitting in a circle further reinforces equality. To emphasize the importance of equality we say, "Leave your hat at the door."

These principles were illustrated in the diagram on the facing page by social worker Sabine Tibetts, who co-leads Recovery Dialogue sessions at Riverside Community Care in Wakefield, Massachusetts. Note that in this illustration the principle of suspension of beliefs is at the top of the circle. One person is thinking to herself, "I believe that ooxxoo," while the other person is thinking to himself, "I believe that xxyyxx." Generally, but not always, women are from the emotional world and men from the logical world. This may be one reason why our eCPR classes only have about 15% men. (Another reason may be that our participants are drawn from the human services world, which has a greater percentage of women.)

The following suggested steps for setting up a Recovery Dialogue emerged after many sessions held at Riverside Community Care.

- Pick co-facilitators, one of whom is a person with lived experience. They should both be comfortable *facilitating*, not leading, groups.
- Find a few champions of Recovery Dialogues within your organization who hold management level positions and have influence. Encourage them to talk it up.
- Hold a planning meeting with someone experienced at conducting Recovery Dialogues (or someone with an understanding of dialogical principles), fellow champions, and the co-facilitator.

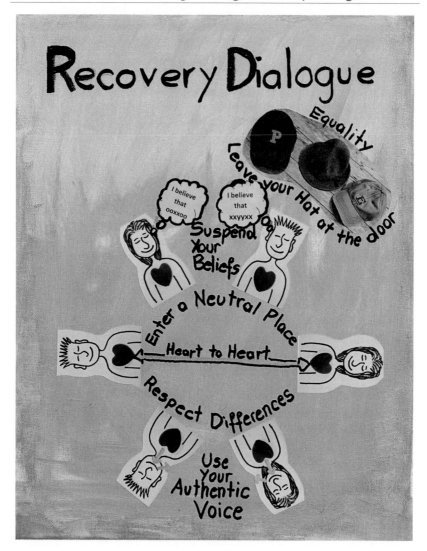

- Decide on the participants for a Recovery Dialogue session. Select a suitable time and place that will accommodate at least ten to twenty participants in a circle. Produce an announcement flyer, and plan ahead to obtain the necessary beverages or refreshments.
- Convey outreach with respect. Make it understood that during the session there will be no right or wrong answers and no agenda. Relate that the objective is to introduce principles of dialogue and

that everyone attending should abandon any fear of being judged when they walk through the door.

- Obtain administrative commitment and financial support; ensure accommodations for staff time and any facilitators who will attend.
- Since much emotional communication is conveyed nonverbally, it is essential that everyone be seated in a circle and that they be able to see and hear each other easily and clearly. This arrangement is best achieved with fewer than twenty people.
- It is often helpful to begin a session with an ice-breaker that connects on an emotional level. Introducing each other by first names keeps status and roles outside of the room. It is helpful if co-facilitators have a clear understanding of the six principles of dialogue. They may start by focusing on a specific theme, such as recovery, spirituality, or how to strengthen community. Otherwise, it is best to have no set agenda; let the group create the conversation.
- Hand out evaluation forms at the end of the session to gather feedback.

I facilitated Recovery Dialogues for four years. There are now four ongoing monthly dialogues at Riverside Community Care. These dialogues are beginning to produce sustainable culture change in this mental health center. There is movement in the expectations of staff and persons with lived experience, from maintenance to recovery. I am humbled by how much I learn at each meeting. By starting without an agenda, and "leaving our hats at the door," we are learning to genuinely connect on our most equal and human level. The process allows us to start to think together and new, unexpected feelings and thoughts emerge. I am amazed at how every person, no matter what their position in life or place in recovery, has much to offer the group.

Testimonials by Two Participants in Recovery Dialogues

Initially, the day we hosted a Recovery Dialogue session was no different than any other. I had a hundred things to do and not enough time to do them. When I saw Steve Goldman, a Peer Specialist, preparing the circle of seats I breathed in deeply and let out a huge sigh of relief. A huge smile took over my face.

While the concept of discussing recovery may sound simplistic, it is much more. It is an opportunity to meet on an equal basis regardless if you are a provider or an individual receiving services. It provides a place to actively listen. Sometimes your way of thinking may be challenged, or the complexity of your experiences may be validated. It is a place to share struggles and strategies honestly from the heart without judgment.

At the conclusion of the session, I experienced a renewed sense of hope. It confirmed that we all are people first and we are truly never alone. We have come so far in seeing the whole person in the holistic approach of recovery. Recovery Dialogues are the catalyst we need to evolve our mental health system. They allow the participants — both those who provide or receive direct services as well as those that hold the power to enact reform — to challenge the archaic systems that still exist. — Danielle Ford-Allen, Director of Neponset Clubhouse, Neponset, Massachusetts

I have experienced Recovery Dialogues during the past two or three years, and they have helped me grow as someone in recovery. As each month passes, I look forward to participating in the new dialogue. Peers, mentors, and other people with lived experience have all shared ideas of wellness and recovery. Each positive topic that we talk about gives me additional ideas about how I can help others and myself with any challenges that may arise.

The sessions I have attended are usually composed of groups of seven to fifteen people who together listen and share their stories of hope and tales of troubled times. As I actively listen to everyone, I try to impart what has worked for me. The Recovery Dialogue sessions are a place where people can be honest and speak from their hearts. Everyone is an equal: people with lived experience, providers, and colleagues. — Steve Goldman, peer specialist, Riverside Community Care, Wakefield, Massachusetts

TEN

Facilitating Recovery of Life
through Open Dialogue

Open Dialogue is a clinical approach that comes the closest to implementing the principles of recovery. It is based on a new way of thinking: Open Dialogue does not suppose that problems are located in an individual's brain — as the present medical model does — nor that the problem resides with the family of a person with severe distress — as traditional systemic family therapy does. Instead of locating a problem, Open Dialogue looks at each social network as a whole in which everyone evolves together.

One of the most important reasons for the heightened worldwide interest in Open Dialogue is that its practitioners have reported the best recovery rates in the world for individuals with first-episode psychosis.

In a five-year study of Open Dialogue, 86% of individuals had returned to their studies or a full-time job, 18% of individuals had residual psychotic symptoms, and 14% were on disability allowance. Only 29% had used neuroleptic medication in some phase of their treatment. In comparison, after two-years in a traditional program, only 21% of individuals were working or returned to studies, 50% had residual symptoms, and 57% were on disability allowance. 100% of individuals in the traditional program were prescribed neuroleptics at some point in the two-year period.

The terrific results of Open Dialogue have motivated a number of us to work on replicating Open Dialogue in the U.S. This will be challenging for multiple reasons. Perhaps the biggest barrier is the deep-seated belief in this country that psychiatric problems are primarily due to a brain dysfunction.

Mary Olson, Jaakko Seikkula, Doug Ziedonis, and I are members of a group in the United States that is working to adapt the Open Dialogue approach in this country. Olson and Seikkula have described two distinct areas of the practice, which they call the *poetics* and the *politics* of Open Dialogue. The poetics are the principles of the practices Open Dialogue and the politics are the organization of the services that facilitate the delivery of Open Dialogue.

The Politics of Open Dialogue

The development of Open Dialogue resulted from a trio of accomplishments. The first occurred in 1984, when treatment meetings were organized in a hospital in Tornio, Finland, to replace systemic family therapy. Later, in 1987, a crisis clinic was founded in the same hospital to organize case-specific teams for inpatient referrals. Finally, in 1990, all the regional mental health outpatient clinics near Tornio, Finland, started to organize mobile crisis intervention teams.

The Finnish practitioners of Open Dialogue have described seven main treatment principles that emerged from the training and research programs that they have undertaken. These principles cover the ways services are organized in Open Dialogue.

- **The provision of immediate help.** Clinics arrange the first meeting within 24 hours of the first contact. The initial contact may come from the "person of focus" (their description of the person in distress), a relative, or a referral agency.
- **A social network perspective.** Persons of concern, their families, and other key members of the person's social network are always invited to the initial meetings to mobilize support for the person and their family. Other key members may include workers from official agencies, such as the local employment and health insurance agencies that support vocational rehabilitation, fellow workers, or neighbors and friends.

- **Flexibility and mobility.** These are guaranteed by adapting a therapeutic response to the specific and changing needs of each network.
- **Responsibility.** The staff member who is the first contact becomes responsible for organizing the initial meeting. It is during this early meeting that decisions about treatment are made.
- **Psychological continuity.** The team is responsible for treatment in both outpatient and inpatient settings. (Its duration is defined as "for as long as it takes.") Members of the person's social network are invited to participate in meetings throughout the treatment process.
- **Tolerance of uncertainty.** Building a relationship in which all parties can feel safe strengthens the capacity for tolerance of uncertainty. In psychotic crises, holding a meeting every day during the first ten-to-twelve days appears necessary to generate an adequate sense of security. Tolerance of uncertainty is an active attitude among the therapists. They live and work together with the network and aim to achieve a joint process.
- **Dialogism.** The primary focus of Open Dialogue is on promoting interaction, and secondarily on promoting change in the person or the family. The dialogical conversation is seen as a forum where families and persons in distress have the opportunity to increase their sense of agency by gaining a new understanding among the participants. Instead of having some specific interviewing procedure, the team's aim in constructing the dialogue is to follow the themes and the manner of communication that the family members are used to.

The Poetics of Open Dialogue

The following is a summary of the philosophy of Open Dialogue that was compiled by Mary Olson and Jaakko Seikkula in my class with them in 2013. I added three more observations based upon my experience working with them:

- Use open-ended questions, which work to expand the conversation and broaden points of view. An example would be starting with the question, "How would you like to use this time?"

- Respond to every utterance. According to Mikhail Bakhtin, in life there is nothing worse than no response.
- Try to achieve conversations reflecting attention, use of images, resonance of emotions, and movement.
- Polyphony values multiple points of view and differing perspectives. This helps the transition from "either/or" to "both/and" thinking.
- Be in the present moment. As Bakhtin observed, "We live in the once occurring participation of being."
- Value transparency. Say your thoughts out loud. All planning should be done openly and in the presence of the person in distress.
- Understand that what may seem abnormal can be understandable in the context of its culture.
- Engage the larger world by bringing into the conversation significant people who are absent. Include members of someone's larger social network. For instance: "If so and so were here, what might they say about — —?"
- Place emphasis on current stories rather than on symptoms.
- Act as a fellow collaborator rather than as an expert; leave your social role at the door.
- Be as attentive to embodied gestures or utterances as to spoken words. Work to be aware of the spaces between people and what they communicate rather than centering on what is going on inside them.
- Widen understanding by opening the conversation to include statements that are speculative or invoke curiosity and wonder. Work to limit conversation that suggests certainty or finality.

To elaborate upon the last three points, I will contrast common clinical practice with that of dialogical practice, highlighting their differences.

Working as a Collaborator, Rather than as an Expert

Conventional Clinical Practice: Most clinicians practicing conventional therapy today enter the client/doctor relationships in the role of the expert. Most clients expect the clinician to assume this role. Yet this expert-driven approach to care ultimately results in clients being disempowered and many clinicians feeling exhausted. Ultimately, no one really wants to be told what to do, despite what they might request at the outset. Furthermore, no one really knows what is best for another person. Though they may not believe it, the person in distress knows the best path to relief. Clinicians, generally, conduct initial interviews to gather data, and later formulate a diagnosis separately from the person and their network.

Once the clinician has settled on a diagnosis, she/he usually sees all of the person's thoughts and behavior through the lens of that diagnosis. The clinician's expert position reinforces monological thinking, or what John Shotter, a communications professor at the University of New Hampshire, has called "aboutness thinking." It is monological because there is only one version of the expert's story "about" the other person. That version is a mental illness story, a master narrative constructed primarily by the clinician. Aboutness thinking makes the person into an object that has no consciousness of their own. It is a static and dead approach. It invalidates the voice of the person in distress, their family, and indeed any team member of lesser status.

The degree of collaboration can also be understood from the standpoint of language. In classical psychoanalysis, the client had to learn the language of the analyst. In strategic family therapy, the therapist starts by learning the language of the client, but with the intent of engaging the client in the language and concepts of the therapist.

Open Dialogue Approach: In Open Dialogue, the clinician strives to be as equal as possible with the "person of focus" and their network. The clinician enters from a position of not knowing. The clinician believes that there is truth and value in every utterance spoken by each person in the network. The clinician is humble, and recognizes that the challenges from their own past always color their understanding of the difficulties facing others. They enter with compassion. The American Buddhist teacher and author Pema Chödrön has written, "Compassion is not a relationship between the healer and the wounded. It is the relationship between equals. Only when we know our own darkness well, can we be present with the darkness of others. Compassion becomes real when we realize our shared humanity."

To be collaborative is to be dialogical. To be collaborative is to be in the present moment as defined by Mikhail Bakhtin. To be collaborative is what John Shotter describes as *withness* thinking as opposed to *aboutness* thinking. "Withness thinking," Shotter writes, "is a dynamic form of reflective interaction that involves coming into contact with another's living being, with their utterances, with their bodily expressions, with their works." Klaus Deisler, a clinician using dialogical practice in Germany, has described collaborative therapy as dialogical collaboration. When people understand that they are equal in power or status, Deisler observes, "being at the same level makes people relate in a new way, and you can create a new language."

Personally, this is the type of therapist I yearned for while trapped in my own monological world during my twenties — and I had the good fortune to find such a therapist. He always reminded me that we were on a joint venture. Anytime I complimented him on an insight he would say sincerely that it came from me.

I carry this collaborative spirit with me when I am seeing people with their networks. Recently, my teammate, Karen, I, and the person of focus were reviewing our therapy. A year earlier, conventional therapists would have classified this client as manic.

As he started to reflect on that period, he said, "Remember a year ago when I was..." He hesitated. My impulse was to say, "When you were manic," but I paused and let him continue, curious and eager to learn how he experienced that period of time.

"When I developed an expanded view," he said.

That heartfelt utterance opened our eyes to the positive side of what conventional therapists would have seen as a sign of his illness.

Being Attentive to Embodied Gestures

Conventional Clinical Practice: Conventional therapy focuses on the verbal/cognitive dimension of communication in which words and sentences are considered in isolation, separated from their emotional context. Specific spoken words are the primary concern in most therapies. With the exception of Gestalt therapy, little value is given to the gestures that accompany the spoken words. The therapist determines meaning based upon his or her own frame of reference, attempting to objectively analyze sentence structure according to its linear logic. A person is classified as psychotic if their speech is not rational, as judged by its conformity to linear logic. A person who does not speak is considered catatonic, and communication is considered impossible.

Once again, I return to my own experience at Bethesda Naval Hospital to offer an illustration of the striking contrast between traditional therapy and a more dialogical approach. I had stopped talking, eating, and moving. Conventional therapists could not reach me. Eventually, it was the least trained provider, a corpsman, who reached me by connecting almost completely on an emotional, nonverbal level rather than on the verbal level.

Open Dialogue Approach: Three important interrelated concepts of Open Dialogue are *embodiment, utterances,* and *addressivity* (or *responsiveness* sought in the person being spoken to). Open Dialogue comes via a verbal exchange of embodied words. "Embodiment" of language means that the meaning of what someone says is found in their emotional expression — as communicated in body language — as well as in the symbols the words represent. A responsive listener actively gains meaning from utterances expressed by the speaker. The listener does this by being attuned to the emotional tone of the speaker's voice.

The Swedish linguist Per Linell describes utterances very well in his book *Rethinking Language:*

> *Within linguistics, language has nearly always been portrayed as something abstract and formal, immaterial and impersonal . . . But language lives in and through the languaging of real people in their interacting with one another. The utterances of language users are always embodied. They consist of material words, enacted by embodied individuals and carried by their voices. When a person fills his language with life, he or she adds prosody (intonation, accent, rhythm . . .) and voice quality to it, producing utterances.*
>
> *Utterances are always the product of and determinant of social situations: the immediate social situation and the broader social milieu [that] wholly determine — and determine from within, so to speak — the structure of an utterance.*

Mikhail Bakhtin pointed out that utterances are actually units of communication. To understand language as a living process, Bakhtin turned his attention to the study of whole utterances. Utterances are real, responsive, interactive units determined by a change of speaking subjects. Any utterance has an absolute beginning and an absolute end. The speaker ends his utterance to make room for the other's responsive, active understanding. Utterances not only belong to real, embodied people, they also elicit a response from the one addressed. Bakhtin referred to this as the responsiveness or addressivity of the utterances. Every utterance has an addressee or second party whose responsive understanding is being sought. Addressivity extends beyond actual participants in dialogue to include real or imagined others for whom the utterance is meant, and from whom a responsive understanding is sought. Utterances are related to one another in a chain-like fashion, where each utterance gives meaning to every other utterance.

The following example illustrates this concept. When Mark came to see me a year ago he was in a very distressed state. He seemed trapped in monologue. His words lacked an emotional tone; they were not embodied. He seemed in his own world, with little regard for my presence. His words lacked addressivity as they apparently were not addressed to me or anyone else.

On the next visit I invited in Mark's nephew. When his nephew joined us, Mark changed his demeanor and his way of relating. His words were expressed with an emotional tone that made them embodied utterances directed to his nephew. He showed delight in the book that his nephew was reading. His utterances were expressed with intent to elicit a response from his nephew: they exemplified addressivity. He was speaking as a listener.

A year later, when Mark was better able to reflect, we spoke about this moment. I noted my surprise when I saw him relax and relate naturally with his nephew, whereas he had been so distressed and preoccupied when he was alone with me. He said I should not have been surprised that he was able to relate spontaneously with his nephew. "After all," he said, "I know my nephew much better than I know you. We share a number of common interests, including the science fiction book my nephew brought him with him that day." (Below I include a more detailed description of a set of open dialogue sessions.)

Widen Understanding with Speculative Statements; Accept Uncertainty

Conventional Clinical Practice: In conventional therapy, most clinicians begin by defining a person's diagnosis based on a set of symptoms. Within several visits the clinician looks up the set of symptoms in psychiatry's bible, the *Diagnostic and Statistical Manual of Mental Disorders*, or DSM. After the person's problem is defined according to the DSM, the clinician develops a treatment plan. All treatment is designed to reduce the severity of the symptoms.

It is not uncommon for a clinician to describe the identity of the person as the diagnosis itself, referring to the person as "a bipolar" or "a schizophrenic." It is not unusual for clients to introduce themselves this way. If someone introduces her/himself to me, "I am bipolar," I encourage her to instead say, "I am Mary, who has been diagnosed with bipolar disorder." Adopting the identity of a diagnosis may initially reduce the anxiety of not knowing what is wrong when someone is in distress. But the damaging effect is that it precludes further inquiry into the deeper nature of the difficulty and the need to gather a variety of points of view to broaden our understanding of the person and their network. **This finality and finite quality of a psychiatric diagnosis robs a person of hope and growth.**

Open Dialogical Approach: Mikhail Bakhtin was very suspicious of theories and ideology. Theories have a way of closing down dialogue by concluding that there are answers when only possibilities exist. He argued that thoughts should not have a final conclusion, but instead need to be open-ended, or "unfinalizable." He believed that there is in life a greater importance in little details than in grand scale generalizations, such as in science, which he called super-addressivity. He called the little details of life, "the prose of everyday life." In explaining unfinalizability, he wrote, "Nothing conclusive has yet taken place in the world; the ultimate word of the world and about the world has not yet been spoken; the world is open and free; everything is still in the future and will always be in the future." He uses the term unfinalizability to mean openness, creativity, and surprise. This idea generates hope.

The clinicians of Open Dialogue achieve unfinalizability in a variety of ways, all of which increase the agency of the person of focus and their network. In the beginning of an Open Dialogue session, clinicians usually ask each member of the network the story behind the meeting, the reason for which it was assembled, and why each person is in attendance. The team will next ask the network how they would like to use their time. This way the agenda is set by the network itself, and not by the clinicians. The posture and intonation of the clinicians usually leans towards curiosity and wonder.

After witnessing sessions with the Finnish Open Dialogue psychologists and Mary Olson, it is my impression that they genuinely do not have preconceptions about the problem and what will be the best course of action. There is always a tentative quality to their observations and a questioning of themselves, as well as the network. Open Dialogue tries to elicit as many opinions as possible. Indeed, opinions are not confined to those held by people in the room. One may prompt a discussion by asking speculatively about what another member of the network who is not physically present might say.

I think two quotations from the playwright Eugène Ionesco nicely sum up the Open Dialogue approach:

Explanation separates us from astonishment, which is the only gateway to the incomprehensible.

Ideologies separate us. Dreams and anguish bring us together.

Explanations and ideologies are "finalizable." Perhaps the Open Dialogue approach is designed to keep a sense of astonishment and wonder present, to keep open the gateway to the incomprehensible. I would add a corollary: We need to watch the response of the audience to be sure that the difference in understanding that we are proposing is not too different from that which people are accustomed to thinking. Otherwise there is great resistance.

Tom Andersen believed that conventional therapy tends to emphasize modes of reality that Andersen referred to as "the visible and static," which he equated with "either-or" thinking. The conventional therapist defines the person being treated as conforming to a specific diagnosis; behavior is explained by the therapist's formulation of the person's true motives and dynamics. An Open Dialogue approach is based on what Andersen referred to as the "invisible and movable" aspects of life, the world of "both/and" thinking. This is the world of relationships that are best described by metaphors and poetry. A good example can be found in e.e. cummings's famous poem, "since feeling is first:"

since feeling is first
who pays any attention
to the syntax of things
will never wholly kiss you

In the Open Dialogue approach, it is recommended that gestures be described rather than explained. Images are valued, as they often describe the idea of possibilities better than words. For instance, Professor Shotter has described the early aspects of a meeting like multiple rivulets that later form a stream or river. It appears we all need to stay close to a growing edge of new awareness and to learn through our relationships, both within us and with others. This growing edge enables us to be continually present, to see new broader perspectives, and to express our own distinct personal Voice. It enables us to evolve — along with our community of trusted friends and family — to more fully express ourselves. The outcomes of the Open Dialogue approach refer back to the degree by which they enable the person and their network to achieve this co-evolving Self.

The Finnish Open Dialogue practitioners say their purpose is to help the person of focus and their network get a grip on life. This is similar to our movement's description of recovery, which has been expanded to embrace the words "Recovery of Life."

How does the Open Dialogue approach enable someone to get a grip on life? The task of the Open Dialogue team is to gently connect with someone and assist them and their network in their transition into dialogue. There is something about being in dialogue that enables each of us to get a grip on life. In the words of one of my clients, the team helps each of the members of the network gain a broader view of themselves and of each other. In doing so, they can start to practice the process of dialogue and form a more cohesive network and community. Collaboration with therapists appears to be essential because the network is often not capable of changing itself. My client observed that his family was able to see that he was contributing in a positive fashion only in the presence of the network therapists.

The typical clinical approach can be understood as a monologue which is static and final. Moving away from monologue toward dialogue fosters an increasing appreciation of the world as a series of never-repeated present moments. I suspect we naturally resist this idea because of our fear of death. Like Ozymandias in Shelley's poem by the same name, we think we can achieve immortality by creating works and ideas that will last for eternity. This need for immortality becomes all the more desperate in times of crisis because we start to sense the life forces draining from us. The poem describes the shattered statue of an ancient king, on the pedestal of which were written these hollow words:

My name is Ozymandias, king of kings:
Look on my works, ye Mighty, and despair!
Nothing beside remains.

The recovery movement in the United States and around the world beautifully complements the Open Dialogue approach. eCPR, which was created by peers to address a need to facilitate recovery, can greatly enhance the Open Dialogue approach. Yet convincing a family in their hour of need that a non-expert-driven and open-to-uncertainty approach works better than the present day standard of care is difficult. **How do you convince them that they are already carrying the resources for healing when they are crying out for an expert in a white coat to save them? The key element appears to be making an initial constructive connection; getting the person and the team doing the assisting to connect with the person in distress and their network.**

We have been addressing the importance of making the initial connection in eCPR, and have found that the emotional dimensions expressed in nonverbal communication are the most critical. When crisis erupts, words become suspect and are no longer trusted. The person doing the assisting needs to convey assurance by their posture, by their tone of voice, through their eyes and their facial expression, by their breathing, and with their overall demeanor. This approach tells the person in distress that the assisters will be there, that they will stay with them, and that they believe in them. Those doing the assisting need to be able to communicate to all those in distress with full, emotionally enriched words. They must do so in a manner that demonstrates that collaboration is possible and that life can return if the members of the network connect with them and with each other. Once the network feels that it can trust the team, members of the network can experience their own power; then revitalization of the network as a whole can occur.

Observations and Participation in Open Dialogue Practice in Finland

In the summer of 2013, I accompanied teams of Finnish Open Dialogue practitioners as they conducted five sessions with their clients. In each instance, in Open Dialogue fashion, I shared some of my own lived experience. Here are my conclusions from the rich experience:

- Many experienced practitioners of Open Dialogue apply their practice based on years of experience. They utilize methods that they may not have fully articulated to themselves. There is no established guidebook or manual.

- Open Dialogue creates an environment for incorporating a variety of voices with a variety of points of view, including peers with shared experience.

- Open Dialogue opens space for people to speak. I observed one Open Dialogue team working with a mother and her twenty-six-year-old son who had been hospitalized several times. During each hospitalization, he had only been given medication. They had relocated to Tornio in hopes of receiving Open Dialogue treatment. On this day, the young man did not want to leave his room. The team decided they would just talk with his mother in voices loud enough so the young man could listen. Gradually he became curious, joined the others, and shared some stories about their recent travels. When the young man volunteered that he was often occupied by fantastic thoughts during the day, the team listened respectfully but did not inquire as to their nature or focus on any symptoms. The young man entered and exited the room often but the team members did not appear concerned about his movements. Whenever he returned, they would gently re-engage with him and his mother. They did not focus on his past or medication. Instead they focused intently on being with him. At one point, the young man brought in a bowl of apples from his grandfather's farm. At the end of the hour his mother was delighted. She said her son had spoken more in that hour than in the preceding month.

- The Open Dialogue team creates a collaborative relationship with the network. Team members often make home visits and always introduce themselves by their first names and shake hands. They easily transition from a network meeting to one that is more social. One team member mentioned to me that it is essential to know when to change from a network meeting to something more social, such as moving to the kitchen for coffee and pastries. That part of the visit builds trust for future meetings. However, she observed, it was more productive to engage in the social visit after the network meeting had been completed.

- The person of focus in an Open Dialogue session is often appreciative of the way in which the meetings help them relate to others within their network. One young man said he liked having his mother attend some of the meetings because these sessions gave him a better understanding of how she views him and views herself. As a result, it also helps the young man understand how he interacts with his mother. He said that without the team he was unable to see aspects of their relationship clearly. Now that he more fully understands how they relate to each other, he can be with her in a healthier relationship.

- Open Dialogue team members demonstrate that they are willing and interested in learning new information. I observed that, in an effort to create safe relationships with people in distress and their networks, Open Dialogue teams expand their sessions by sharing new ideas and stories with the person of focus and with their network. Forging new bonds enables people in distress and their team learn unconventional ways of interacting and thinking.

- Despite the use of Open Dialogue in Finland, experienced team members occasionally encounter a person of focus who has already been given forced medication by a psychiatrist, even in situations when the person was not demonstrating any indications of violence. In a case that I observed, two team members resolved to give more training to the psychiatrist who ordered the injection of medication to avoid a similar response in the future. They said that the new psychiatrist "needed to live with greater uncertainty."

- I asked the team when they used "reflecting" conversations. They said that the way they use reflection depends upon on the specific situation. One team member reported that reflecting conversations occurred more often when an impasse arose during the Open Dialogue meeting. If one member of the team notices that the other team member is repeatedly asking a similar question and is receiving the same response, they may transition to a reflecting conversation. One therapist recalled that she reflected to her teammate, "I notice that you keep raising your interest in holistic health but wonder if that is the family's interest." This reflective comment seemed to unstick the conversation with the network.

An Example of the Open Dialogue Approach in My Clinical Practice

The following is a description of the application of the Open Dialogue approach in therapy sessions for a family. I had seen an individual in the family for many years for medication maintenance. Karen is someone with lived experience who graduated from the Open Dialogue class with me and worked as a co-therapist with this family, starting in session three. Earlier I have referred to ways in which Mark was helped by Open Dialogue.

How Open Dialogue Likely Prevented Two Institutionalizations

Background: I had been Mark's medication doctor for fifteen years. He had been hospitalized on several occasions for mania prior to my working with him but had not been hospitalized since then. I had seen him during our work together for twelve years at a clinic but, for the last three years, had seen him privately. He had been taking care of his elderly parents and lived in the basement of their house. He had been relatively stable, attending a monthly support group, and seeing me every two to three months. He was taking a very low dose of a major tranquilizer. Then he became agitated, restless, and developed severe insomnia. He said he was very worried about his father, who was developing dementia. It was becoming difficult to follow Mark's conversation. His mother was recovering from a broken leg. I contacted an Alzheimer's support group but Mark said he was too nervous to attend. He said that neither his brother nor sister, who lived in the area, could help. I contacted the elder services agency and they said they would look into a companion for the father. I told Mark that his father needed a companion. I doubled his major tranquilizer and asked him to see me the next week.

The following week he still was not sleeping well and had become hypomanic. He was confused about my advice. When I asked about the companion, he said he had really liked the suggestion and had taken on the role of his father's companion. He shared that when he shifted from the role of son to his father's companion, his father was much more willing and able to enter into conversation. In other matters, Mark could not focus, emptying his pockets of many random pieces of paper when I asked about when elder services might visit. He got angry and further agitated when he could not find the paper he wanted.

This required me to make a decision. I weighed two different paths.

The Path Not Taken — The Conventional Approach

As a psychiatrist in solo practice, my conventional options were very limited. I was thinking, "He is becoming hypomanic and he will need intensive individual treatment. He clearly needs more support than I am able to provide. I will have to refer him to the local hospital ER immediately." Their crisis team would probably have recommended hospitalization for "medication adjustment." Then the hospital staff would have convinced the client and his family that the problem had resulted from reduced antipsychotic medication (gradual though it was). Mark would have been hospitalized for several weeks to increase his medication under close clinical supervision. He would have been discharged to the clinic for individual therapy and case management.

The constant focus would have been on Mark and how to reduce his symptoms of hypomania. Very little attention would have been paid to his social network. The treating clinicians would be thinking, "His hypomania needs medication management. Once he is stable, we will continue him in the monthly support group with a case manager to ensure he takes his medication." The hospital might want him to see one of their psychiatrists to ensure that Mark was maintained on an adequate dose of medication. The hospital might also have had Mark's father transferred to a nursing home, having concluded that Mark could no longer take care of his father.

The Path Taken — The Open Dialogue Approach

Session One: Attended by Mark, his nephew, and myself. Although I was a psychiatrist in solo practice, I had completed seventy-five hours of Open Dialogue training, and thought differently about Mark's agitation. Instead of focusing only on Mark, I started asking questions of his network of potential support. His nephew had driven him to the last two visits. On the first visit he had dropped his uncle off. On the second visit, a week later, he parked his car and walked with his uncle to the steps leading up to my office. As I invited Mark in, his nephew lingered with great concern on his face. I interviewed Mark briefly and could see he was getting more manic. I then asked him if his nephew could join us. He agreed. I invited his nephew and as soon he sat next to his uncle on the couch in my office, Mark calmed down and could focus his attention. They were sharing an illustrated science fiction book and it turned out they had recently gone to the premiere of the movie based on the book.

So I asked his nephew to fill me in about Mark's family situation. He supplied vital information. He agreed that the responsibilities Mark had assumed while taking care of his parents were too much. Mark's father had started to wander and Mark had to stay awake to prevent his father from leaving the house. He said that his mother (Mark's sister) and his other uncle were willing to help out but they were discouraged from doing so by his grandmother, Mark's mother. Mark seemed surprised and clearly relieved to hear that his brother and sister wanted to help. I then asked Mark if we could call his brother during the session. Mark was eager to do so and wanted to dial his brother himself. I honored that request, wanting Mark to be as actively engaged as possible in the course of the therapy. His brother was glad to be contacted and was willing to come to the next meeting. He said he would make sure his parents attended as well.

In the session with Mark's nephew present, I contacted Mark's mother, who was relieved to hear there would be a family meeting. She agreed to come to the next meeting and bring her husband with her. I then called Mark's sister. She was also eager to help and agreed to come to the next network meeting. By the end of this hour-long meeting, Mark was significantly less agitated — and so was I. I was beginning to believe that Open Dialogue could prevent Mark from being hospitalized.

Course in Open Dialogue: Several days later, I spent four days learning more about Open Dialogue in Mary Olson's class. I volunteered to engage in a role-playing session of Mark and his family. I played Mark and had other students play his family. The role-play was very helpful. It allowed me to think about Mark's mother in a new way. Instead of focusing on her as a source of interference with outside help, I could appreciate that she was being protective of her husband, and perhaps worried that accepting outside help might result in his being placed in a nursing home. I also could experience the relief Mark might feel about getting assistance from his siblings. Over all, the role-playing session made me less apprehensive about meeting the larger family. It also helped me be more dialogical in my thinking.

Session Two: Attending: Mark, brother Rob, sister Carol, mother Regina, father Clyde, co-therapist Karen, and myself. I started the meeting by asking the family, "What do you want to get from this meeting?" Regina, immediately responded, "I want to know if it has been too much for Mark to take care of us." Soon a major issue was identified: Clyde's wandering out of the house when no one was look-ing. Recently he had watched a television show that reminded him of his mother, and not long afterwards, he disappeared from the house. After much searching by Mark, he found his father in a nearby store looking for milk. Regina mentioned that most of their friends have died. Rob suggested that they put a deadbolt on the one door that Clyde might use to escape. But then Regina said she was already feel-ing like a prisoner in her own house. When I asked why, she held up a handful of keys.

Regina mentioned that one reason Mark could not sleep was that he felt he needed to be on alert to his father's wandering. Rob said that he and Carol appreciate that Mark has been very helpful. They were fearful to share this sentiment with Mark, as they thought he might experience it as pressure to do more. Rob and Carol said they would be glad to offer additional help. Regina replied that they were both too busy to help; Rob works a night shift in a factory, while Carol works as an administrative assistant at an insurance company.

There were two areas where Regina did not want help. Regina said flatly she did not want anyone else doing their housework or laundry. Regina, however, admitted that it is hard for her to ask for help. This re-luctance of Regina's, combined with the fact that Mark finds it difficult to say 'no' to his parents' requests, leads to many of their problems.

At the end of the session, I asked if there was anything else they wanted to say. Mark shared that he was worried that if his siblings were helping he would not be needed any more. I made an analogy to the procedure for using oxygen masks on an airplane. I reminded him that airlines always urge parents to inhale a breath of oxygen before giving the mask to a child. In this case, Mark needed a breather so he could more readily take care of his parents.

Session Three: Attending: Mark, Carol, Rob, Regina, Clyde, Karen, and myself. This session took place two weeks after Session Two. "How would you like to use this time?" I asked. The family was eager to report on their progress. Mark said the woman from the Alzheimer's support group had been very helpful. She had given him information about the support group and he now felt ready to attend. The woman from elder services suggested that Mark's father go to a day program for veterans. Mark thought he should go with him as a transition. Then he said he might even volunteer there. Mark's brother had taken the parents for a weekend and had gone grocery shopping with Mark's mother. (There was some joking about how many hours it took to take Regina shopping.) Mark said he now transfers the laundry from the washing machine to the dryer, but always under the watchful eye of his mother.

Karen commented on how much they cared about each other, to which they all agreed. They asked her if they seemed to be more troubled than most families. She said, "No. Actually, you were able to come together faster than most families I have observed." In fact, we both pointed out that their genuine caring for each other might be a factor that is enabling this approach to work: they were able to call upon a high degree of cohesion and support that existed prior to the period of stress.

After this discussion about the family's collaboration and support, Mark inquired why it had been necessary to have his family come to these sessions. We turned that question back to the family. They said in general they felt it had been helpful. Carol then looked at us and nodded to her mother sitting next to her, and said, "And it was particularly important that someone in the family hear that it was important for the family to get some outside assistance." We asked who had needed to hear that. Mark's mother immediately knew that her daughter meant her. She defended herself, half-heartedly, saying,

"Well, I didn't realize what a stress it was on Mark." Mark responded by questioning Carol, asking if his new request for assistance had been a burden on his family. Carol said caringly, "No, far from it. You have been a great assistance to our parents and we can see you need a rest." Karen and I reinforced this message. I said, "In fact, his distress was a gift to his family because it alerted us that his father needs outside assistance. Had we not learned this, your father might have had greater problems."

Mark seemed very satisfied with this response. Overall he was much more alert and better able to interact. His agitation had greatly subsided. He wanted to start driving again. The family then reported that in fact, Mark had already started to take short drives in the neighborhood. They all felt he was ready for such drives, so we validated that idea.

The rest of the meeting was devoted to drawing out Mark's father. He wears a World War II hat with the dates he was in the Navy, 1943–45, and lit up at mention of the war. He was seventeen when he enlisted. Many men in his company couldn't stand the pressure and went home, he said. "But I couldn't leave because my father was an officer in the Navy. He told me, 'You better not come back!'" The rest of the family chimed in that their grandfather had been very strict.

I concluded with a request that Mark call me a week later to check in with any news about how he and his family were doing.

Conclusion from Session Three: It appears this family made great progress in just two network meetings. The family rallied to help the trio of Mark and his parents. Mark is no longer hypomanic. He is no longer the focus of the problem. Instead, it has been understood by everyone that these challenges affect the relationships existing between all members of the family. By facilitating better dialogue among the members of the family, they were able to accept outside help. A critical player was Mark's mother. She needed to come to the conclusion that she and her husband needed more assistance than Mark could provide. Once she heard that observation voiced by the therapists, she reassessed the situation and changed her mind, something her children were not able to effect on their own. After Mark's mother agreed that additional assistance was needed, she was able to accept help from her other children and outside agencies. It is likely that these network meetings prevented Mark from being hospitalized and prevented Mark's father being placed in a nursing home.

Phone Call One Week Later: Mark called and said he was doing much better. He said the family was closer to getting his father into the day program. He wondered if his whole family needed to come the next visit. He thanked me, and said the added help was a great relief to him. I requested one more family visit. "If it goes well we will return to sessions with you alone." He was fine with that.

Session Four — One Month Later: Attending: Mark, Clyde, Karen, and myself. Mark continued to improve. He was able to drive again and reported he was getting along much better with his father. They were taking long walks. He wanted to have his father join a day program, but his mother objected. He brought up this issue at the Alzheimer's support group and they recommended that he not tell his mother everything—a new idea for him. So he is going ahead with the referral without her permission. We also discussed the question of his brother's and sister's assistance. He said they were not as involved now as they had been when he was in crisis. He did say that he was feeling pressure rising at home between himself and his mother. I turned to the Karen and commented, "It seems to help to see that these problems are not just his problems but problems that involve other members of the family." Karen, wondered that if the crisis was over, did he think it could be helpful to have his family — particularly his mother — attend? Mark said he did not want to bother her, now that he was doing better.

Karen again mentioned that if Mark felt the pressure was rising at home it might be a good idea to include his mother and siblings in the next meeting to decrease that pressure. Again, he resisted that idea, saying that since the crisis was over it was not necessary to have them return. He related that he was thinking a lot about how much trouble he has caused his family. He spoke about when he was eight and his mother took him to a doctor for a physical exam. Perhaps he was restless. At the end of the exam, the doctor told his mother, "You will need to watch this one." Notably, at that point, his father Clyde chimed in, saying that Mark did have problems. He said, "I still have to watch over him."

Conclusion from Session Four: This session illustrated the difficulties encountered when changes are introduced into a family's existing belief structure. In addition, there was Mark's personal conviction that the problems resided with him and did not involve the whole family. Only during the crisis period did Mark and his family accept that it was important to have others in the family attend. Once the crisis appeared to have subsided, the family returned to their earlier beliefs, accepting that it was essentially Mark's own problem.

Six Months Later: Karen and I held a session with Mark alone. He said that he now believed he was doing better and that there was no reason to have other family members come to another session. In this session, Mark reflected on what he learned in the last year. He believed the family sessions helped him and his family to expand their point of view. He learned to see himself as more capable, and he believed his family had changed as a whole. They now saw him as being more worthwhile and more complex. He also said he believed that change such as this could only happen through such a process. Mark talked several times about how reflecting has helped him think differently.

[Here Mark introduces the idea that the past family sessions and the condition he had been in a few months earlier had led him to gain an expanded view of his world]

Dan: ...It was about a year ago when you came, and we got into this more — [I pause, trying to think of the best word and not wanting to use the word "mania."]

Mark: — expanded view.

Dan: Expanded view. Yes, that is a good way to look at it. Yeah, "expanded view"... what does that mean? Expanded view... I think of certain things when I hear the words "expanded view."

Mark: My father had some problems. And I took a look at myself and changed my way of thinking a little bit.

Dan: Karen joined the sessions and that expanded my view.

[In the following sequence, Mark describes the pivotal meeting last year with his sister, brother, and parents. During this meeting, his sister made a statement about Mark and her relationship with him that contributed to this expanded view]

Dan: I think I heard your sister say at one time how grateful she was for all that you were doing.

Mark: Yeah, I understand that. I understand where she is coming from.

Dan: Was it helpful to hear that?

Mark: She probably wouldn't have said it outside of this room. Some things are understood, but go unstated otherwise.

Dan: Sometimes it's good to hear them out loud. It's good for me to hear them out loud.

Mark: Yes, it was meaningful.

Dan: It helped me to hear it out loud. As I recall, you were saying, "I am sorry that I am the problem." And she said, "Far from the problem." [*Dan turns to Karen*] Do you recall what she said?

Karen: She said, "You are not a problem; you are very helpful."

Mark: I remember she said she couldn't see a problem when she looked at me. Problematic is a big word.

Dan: [*Dan looks over at Karen, using a reflecting conversation*] I am thinking maybe it isn't as bad as you think? Maybe your problems aren't as bad as you think. I know that is hard to get beyond.

Karen: I am wondering how many of the things that we think are understood between people are, in actuality, really our own understanding, and *not* a common understanding. When we verbalize what we believe to others, it can be really powerful to know either that you are in agreement, or that your understanding doesn't agree with what others believe to be the situation. Saying it can be amazing.

Dan: [*Dan faces Karen*] You are referring to the fact that when she said it out loud it had a big effect. [*Dan faces Mark*] It had a big effect on me. I say that because I had heard from you, "They just think I have problems." When your sister said you were not the problem, this was a new conversation, which I hadn't heard before. And as you suggest, it sounds as if she hadn't even said it out loud before. Has she said it since then to you? Like a thank you?

Mark: I believe we have more common ground than she thinks. She once said that we have nothing in common but our parents.

Dan: But now you think she might think differently?

Mark: Right. Since then she has been bringing up things she thinks might be of shared interest...

Dan: So, that was a big moment when she said that. It helped change your relationship in a way?

Mark: In a good way, rather than —

Dan: Well, it is interesting because you have asked me, "Why do we have these other members of my family attend the sessions?"

Mark: It expanded. I don't have to explain myself. They wanted to know where I have been for the past seventeen years, and now they know.

[We now move to his relationship with his nephew, and how that relationship expanded his view through sessions here]

Mark: Well, my nephew may think I am a little more complex than he previously thought. He might give me a little more credit than I deserve. He's been helpful.

Dan: So it expanded your family's understanding a little more? Your nephew, in a way, was the first key.

Mark: I could never lean on any sibling or relative. I have always been the lone figure, the little brother. So it was very unusual when I was able to lean on my nephew because he was the only contact I had. Like I said, he has been a great help with my parents and with me. He is still there.

[In the following remarks, Mark mentions that his social network has changed, even though the individuals in it remain the same. Karen points out that he made the first change and then it seems they changed in response to his actions]

Dan: Are your brother and sister a little more attentive in any way?

Mark: Yeah, they are.

Dan: I know that is still an issue.

Mark: A work in progress. What you said was important: they can change too.

Karen: Which one of them?

Mark: As a group, not as individuals.

Dan: That is interesting: as a group.

Mark: Some people carry themselves differently. They see me as carrying myself differently, so maybe they think, "There may be more to him than I know."

Dan: They take you a little more seriously now? They respect you a little more?

Mark: Yeah.

Dan: [*Turns to Karen*] They haven't changed individually, but together.

Mark: If you think of them as a group, my nephew stood out because he was the one I connected with and I relied upon. I had conversations with him when no one else was around. We had common interests. For a long time I was just in the house, not talking with anybody except the clinic [Dan's] group. I was absorbed in my isolation. If you don't reach out and try to understand somebody and try to view things from a different perspective, nothing is going to happen. The pool will be stagnant. [*This is a vivid description of what it can feel like to be trapped in monologue*]

Karen: [*Facing Dan*] I am struck by this description where Mark feels like a passive thing. But I think he took an active role. We talk about dialogue as not just talking with someone, but the process of changing each other. Can we really change other people? In his case, he changed what he thought of himself and others also reacted differently, and that changed what came later. I was struck by the idea that he was kind of a passive thing, but I think he was very active.

Dan: We had to counter the belief that no one would be around to help. "My brother and sister can't do anything because they are too busy."

Mark: You are starting to sound like me.

Dan: But your nephew helped counter that.

Karen: He expanded their view. I remember the stresses Mark was experiencing while trying to help and contribute. That was incredibly stressful.

Conclusion: An Open Dialogue approach prevented Mark from being psychiatrically hospitalized. If that had occurred, it is very likely that his father would have been sent to a nursing home due to his dementia. However, because the family meetings expanded the points of view of Mark and of the others in his family, each came to recognize Mark's role of contributing to the overall welfare of the family. In the process, he gained confidence in himself and his highly agitated state subsided.

Six Months Later: Mark's mother contacted me with the news that she was concerned that Mark was slipping. She reported that he seemed distracted and she feared he might have another "episode." I called a family meeting, suspecting that the load of responsibility was falling on him again. Mark, his parents, and sister attended. Indeed, the family verified that neither his brother nor sister were helping with his parents. His sister blamed their mother for not asking for help, and his mother said she shouldn't have to ask. During the meeting it became evident that they had not been speaking to each other for another reason. I suggested that they think of some way to informally get together. His sister suggested a family picnic.

Two Weeks Later: I saw Mark individually and he reported he was feeling much better. This was related to his mother and sister getting along better after they went on two family picnics. With relations repaired, his sister was able to take on some responsibility and give Mark a break from continuous caretaking. In addition, Mark no longer had to listen to his mother complain about his sister not caring about her.

A Reflection on the Above Open Dialogue Approach in My Clinical Practice

Peers in the U.S. are particularly hopeful about the adopting of Open Dialogue because the values underlying this approach are consistent with those underlying recovery. The more that treatment systems can adopt the Open Dialogue approach, the more fulfilling the work of peers will be. Peers already are playing a vital role in bringing this approach to the attention of decision-makers and funders. Open Dialogue is an essential component of the multi-pronged transformation of the mental health system, which I propose in the next chapter.

ELEVEN

My Thoughts on Recovery of Community Life

Several years ago I had a dream, which may guide all of us through this global darkness of despair:

I was sitting in a circle with about eight to ten peers. We were calmly and attentively communicating with each other in a group. We were practicing eCPR as a group. Meanwhile, all around us were hundreds of "chronically normal" people (those not yet diagnosed), running around with wild expressions and waving their arms in a desperate fashion. Occasionally they would stop running and look at our group, puzzled by our calm and cohesive state. Eventually, one of these chronically normal people inquired about the secret of our composure. When the group members responded that they were just listening and dialoguing with each other, this reply was met with disbelief. "But what drugs are you on? What program are you following?" one of the incredulous people asked. Our group reported that no drugs were involved; we were merely following our hearts and listening to each other with our hearts. Our group was not following a rigidly imposed program. Rather, we were encouraging life to emerge in the present moment. Some who were labeled normal brought in television cameras, but all they could observe was a group of people being very open and human with each other.

This is the message of peer support that we have learned and want to share. **Rather than being viewed as a burden and threat to society, I**

hope for a day when we can be used as a source of valuable information about the extreme emotional states that more and more people are entering into. We have already been there and have come back to share what we have found helpful in recovering our humanity.

I have discovered that it is more fulfilling to live my life attuned to my feelings as they arise than keeping them at a safe distance. I no longer want to think about everything objectively and thus avoid experiencing the world. The noted anthropologist and social scientist Gregory Bateson once wrote, "There are times when I catch myself believing that there is such a thing as something... which is separate from something else." I experienced an epiphany very much paralleling Bateson's words while standing on a rock in a stream when I was twenty-five. I felt connected to all other living beings. I realized, that we are all touching the earth, and through that contact, touching each other. It was a moment of experiencing my "process of living." It was as if I was coming to life after a lifetime of being only half-alive. I felt in touch with my vital center. I sensed for the first time that I fully existed. So I would paraphrase Bateson and say I realize now, "That no living being is separated from any other living being."

At that moment in that stream, I also realized that until then I had separated myself from other people. I believe, at that moment, I connected with a deeper aspect of myself that had stopped growing due to trauma. (In retrospect, I only wish I could have found a less abrupt way to come to that realization.) At that moment, while standing on the rock, I discovered my "mute, inner being," the part of us that Louis Évely alludes to in the meditation I cited in the opening of Chapter Four.

Recently I started a talk on recovery by revisiting Évely's meditation. Below I will examine his words, as they now have even deeper meaning to me:

Loving people means summoning them forth
  with the loudest and most insistent of calls:
it means stirring up in them
  a mute and hidden being
    who can't help leaping at the sound of our voice —

a being so new
> *that even those who carried him*
> *didn't know him,*
> *and yet so authentic*
> *that they can't fail to recognize him*
once they discover him . . .
To love someone is to bid them to live,
> *invite them to grow.*
Since people don't have the courage to mature
> *unless someone has faith in them,*
we have to reach those we meet
> *at the level they stopped developing, . . .*

I did not know that mute, hidden being inside me. Deep inside, I had the sense that I had been living someone else's life, not my own. I was only living the life expected of me. I believed that I had to fulfill the expectations of my family and felt my family history resting heavily on my shoulders. I was frequently reminded that I would be the sixth generation to attend Princeton. In fact, when my friends drove me to the hospital in Baltimore while I was experiencing my first mute state, I was visualizing that family history. I looked up at the stars and imagined they were the eyes of my ancestors looking down on me. They were admonishing me for not fulfilling their expectations. I didn't know that the being inside me did not conform to the idea of the being that I believed they wanted me to be. There was something authentic inside me that was not comfortable with the life of a scientist in a laboratory. As Évely writes, this is a being "so authentic that you can't fail to recognize him once you discover him."

At the time of my crisis, I was beginning to find that being inside me who wanted to be more artistic and to be with people. When an art teacher criticized my rigid conformist sculpture as the creation of an industrialist, he was responding to a visual manifestation of my monological thinking. I had only been living one version of the world: the version that had been handed down to me by my parents and ancestors. This detached me from my authentic Self; I was beginning to say "no" to that life, because I felt dead.

To love someone is to bid them to live,
invite them to grow.

In Open Dialogue, a dialogical space is created among people, from which life emerges. This idea helped me recall my own experience. I was trying to emerge from the "no" space of "no" life. That is why it was so critical that when I was in my darkest hour, I could say "yes" to life after a lifetime of saying "maybe" or "no." This is similar to Bakhtin's idea of unfinalizability. The practice of Open Dialogue avoids a conclusion, a plan, or a solution. When I felt the finality of my thoughts about my life, I had said "no" to life. I often ask audiences what the term "unfinalizable" means to them. Here is a sample of their responses: flexible, changing with the needs of the person, being responsive, open, eternal, no beginning and no end.

The following account by a female peer who works in a psychiatric hospital serves as a good example of how being present and responsive can be important to the (re)creation of life:

"*I observed a recently hospitalized young woman drawing intensely. As we sat together, I also began to draw, and she cried. We shared our interest in spirituality. The woman complained that she had been told that she could get intensive therapy if she came to the hospital. But since she arrived she had only received brief medical checks by a psychiatrist. Then the young woman reported that she had just had an epiphany. She realized that the present moment is vital because it is where life begins. She said she had suddenly come to that idea because of the support I had given her. I told her I had been learning Emotional CPR as a way to support persons in distress. She patted my knee and said, 'Honey, you passed the course.'*"

I found the depth of the experience between these two women very moving. I was also struck by how it points to the importance of the present moment in renewing life and the importance of experiencing the present moment with someone else. As Évely wrote, "People don't have the courage to mature unless someone has faith in them." Interviews that the staff at NEC have conducted reveal that the unwavering presence of someone who has demonstrated belief in the person in crisis has played a vital role in their recovery.

I believe that those in severe emotional distress have suffered an interruption in the development of their lives, just as I did. The deepest trauma that causes this interruption results from a gathering conviction that one cannot be the Self that one most yearns to be. When helping someone recover their life, we need to reach the person at their deepest Self. Again, Évely states this well:

> We have to reach those we meet
> at the level they stopped developing,
> where they were given up as hopeless,
> and so withdrew into
> themselves
> and began to secrete
> a protective shell
> because they thought they were alone
> and no one cared.

Reaching out to those we meet on the emotional level is especially important, for that is inevitably where we stopped growing. As my personal experience with psychosis illustrates, words can lose their meaning. Sometimes the only way to truly reach another person "at the level where they stopped developing" is through nonverbal communication. This is the level of smiles, soothing tones, gentle gestures, and musical notes. This is the level that animals and babies re-teach us, especially in *their* times of need. I am acutely reminded of the importance of nonverbal communication when teaching eCPR. Just as the corpsmen at Bethesda Naval Hospital were able to reach me by communicating that they truly cared, we need to be able to demonstrate that we truly care in order to connect to people who have retreated far inside their protective shell.

It is best if we can reach people at an early stage of their withdrawal. At this point, they are usually still among the people in their social network with whom they can reconnect. This is the beauty of the Open Dialogue approach from Finland. As it is practiced there, Open Dialogue practitioners respond quickly to a person in distress, as well as to their personal network. They persist in connecting until the person and their network can carry on. They realize it is important not to blame families for being unable to supply the connections that are needed. The families themselves are inevitably in acute distress, and often they have retreated into their own protective shells.

Using Dialogical Recovery with a Peer

While writing this book, I was present as two peers and a family member spent five days with a friend as she was experiencing an extreme emotional state. This situation demonstrated to me once again the vital importance of nonverbal peer support. We practiced eCPR and Open Dialogue almost continuously during those five days, as we tried to maintain this extremely important connection. As long as several of us were able to foster this connection, she remained calm and was able to understand simple phrases. However, when one us had to leave or was distracted, she cried out in anguish and pain. At those times she might request that we "tether." We learned from one of the peers, who knew the person in distress's personal meaning, that "tethering" was the word they had developed to indicate connecting by holding hands. Subsequently, we often tethered by holding hands in a circle and maintaining maximum eye contact.

A soothing repetition of phrases uttered by our distressed friend also reinforced the tethering process and strengthened the connections between all of us. I believe that by repeating her phrases we empowered her, as we were also acknowledging her reality. It worked best when she could say, "Tether . . . tether," and we responded by repeating her words and holding hands. This repetition also helped us understand what she was thinking.

At other times, she frequently said, "We have all the time in the world." At first we would repeat the phrase while tethering. Gradually, after watching her response to this repeated phrase, we understood why she had said it. She was trying to remind us that we were speaking and moving too fast; it was her way of saying she felt too hurried. Another phrase she often repeated was, "It's a paradox." We came to understand that the paradox she was alluding to was her desire for voluntary support and no medication, even though her actions required that we encourage her to take medication and seek short-term involuntary hospitalization services.

The Santiago Theory: A Dialogical Approach to Life

My former therapist, George Semchyshyn, recently referred me to the Santiago Theory, revealing that it was personally important to him. While he admitted that it did not inform his practice, he said it reinforced instincts he had learned through life. Here is how Fritjof Capra described the Santiago Theory in his book *The Web of Life*:

> The understanding of the process aspect of living systems . . . implies a new conception of mind, or cognition. This new conception was proposed by Gregory Bateson and elaborated more completely by Maturana and Varela, and it is known as the Santiago theory of cognition.
>
> The central insight of the Santiago theory is the identification of cognition, the process of knowing, with the process of life. Cognition, according to Maturana and Varela, is the activity involved in . . . self-creation, self-making, or self-producing. In other words, cognition is the very process of life.
>
> It is obvious that we are dealing here with a radical expansion of the concept of cognition and, implicitly, the concept of mind. In this new view, cognition involves the entire process of life — including perception, emotion, and behavior — and does not necessarily require a brain and a nervous system.

According to the Santiago Theory of thinking, mind and matter no longer appear to belong to two separate categories. Instead, mind and matter can be seen as representing complementary aspects of the process and structure of life. At all levels of life, beginning with the simplest cell, mind and matter, process and structure, are inseparably connected.

Expanding upon the Santiago Theory, we can see the mistake of narrowly defining mental distress as a form of biological illness due to a chemical imbalance. This formulation denies the process aspect of life. It is shortsighted to claim that a medication by itself will bring mental health. Mental distress can only be understood within the context of our social networks and of all the realms of our existence: mental, physical, social, and spiritual. **Furthermore, the importance of self-creation of living systems reinforces the recovery movement's central principle of self-determination. Recovery is what people do to**

create a new life from within; recovery cannot be done *to* someone or *for* someone.

Dialogue forms a bridge between the worlds of cognition and life. The life activities that the Santiago Theory proposes as cognition are dialogues between living beings and their environment, between living beings, and within living beings. Dialogue gives meaning to the life processes that the Santiago Theory describes as the basis of life. If mental health conditions result from trauma-induced interruptions in life-promoting processes, then it is understandable that dialogue can help in the resumption of those processes.

Proponents of dialogical practice offer greater insight into the propositions of the Santiago Theory. In the interplay of dialogue, new meanings are generated that neither person had previously envisioned. This weaving together of personal worlds expands beyond one's narrow subjectivity and opens new horizons. Ironically, through our shared anguish we are brought together. Through dialogue we can safely share our anguish and we can dream together. Through dialogue we can go beyond the models of thinking that separate us. As Ionesco stated, "Ideologies separate us. Dreams and anguish bring us together."

Building a Healthy World through "Dialogical Recovery of Community Life"

We are facing a grave global crisis. Mental distress is not the exclusive domain of a few unfortunate people. Instead, we see signs of distress in many around our globe, caused by the cumulative, collective traumas we humans have endured during the past century. Once we gained consciousness, we also gained a broader sensitivity to the suffering around us. Together we have been subjected to the traumas of two world wars, a cold war, a war on terrorism, economic inequities, climate change, and much more. . . . A continuous barrage of information — often painful — via the internet amplifies these issues. These traumas have stolen peace and cohesion from our communities. To rebuild our global community, we need a new paradigm of interpersonal communication. We need a new, more evolved consciousness that is based on understanding and respect instead of greed and domination.

Traumas can trap a society into reacting monologically. Under dangerous situations it is useful for a community to unify: attention can be focused on tasks of vigilance and rapid response. However a prolonged fight-or-flight response leads to exhaustion and fragmentation. It can happen to us individually and it can happen to us as a community. A society reacts monologically when its members suppress their emotions and allow those in authority to tell them what to do. Today we are faced with such global dehumanization.

To heal and rebuild communities, I propose a "Dialogical Recovery of Community Life" — a philosophy and set of practices for improving interpersonal communication. This philosophy grows from the shared lived experience of thousands of people around the world who have recovered our lives after enduring extreme emotional distress. We have discovered that people everywhere share the traumas we are recovering from. We also have found that the continued recovery of our lives can only be sustained if all people join with us as citizens of world consciousness. We cannot recover life by ourselves. We need each other in expanding circles of love, trust, and compassion.

As the deadening onslaught of mechanization becomes ever more pervasive, we need to recapture the meaning of being "human." Our collaborative task is to build a peaceful, cohesive world community by shifting from "monological doing" to "dialogical being."

Recovery of Community Life
in Our Traumatized World

Those of us with lived experience of recovery from mental health and addiction conditions can lead a global recovery of life through Dialogical Recovery of Community Life. We need greater support to further develop our leadership capacities. While we have a great deal of collective wisdom, we need to embody what we have learned. I believe there is an urgency to develop such a humanized approach to mental health — and health in general — because dehumanizing corporations are dismantling communities, and communities are the basis of health. They are replacing these cohesive communities with commercialism and consumption. Here are six areas where work is needed right now:

eCPR for everyone. Learning how to dialogue heart-to-heart is the essence of eCPR. Those of us who have been developing eCPR for the last seven years can introduce it more widely without losing the spirit or principles of the approach. It is apparent that those of us with lived experience understand the eCPR approach more deeply than those not yet diagnosed. Therefore, we will need to continue to lead the development and implementation of this approach. However, eCPR can be much more widely used than just for crises. It is also helpful in day-to-day communication. So it will be important to spread the use of eCPR to everyday communication — at home, at work, at play. In fact, one facilitator has suggested that the **R** of eCPR be "Re-creation" or "Recreation." Indeed, we are trying to recreate a humane world community.

Develop and implement Open Dialogue approaches to treat persons with mental health challenges. This very successful approach to treating acute psychosis is starting to be applied to a variety of mental health conditions. But, the Open Dialogue approach faces the challenge of needing to be documented in sufficient detail so that it can be disseminated without losing its essence. Since eCPR complements Open Dialogue, the latter can be taught more readily by learning both practices together. I am part of a team of practitioners centered at the University of Massachusetts Medical School that is working closely with the Finnish developers, who are bringing Open Dialogue to the U.S. while retaining its authenticity.

Medication optimization to reduce mortality among persons with mental health conditions. On average, persons psychiatrically labeled die twenty-five years earlier than the general population. Studies in Finland have shown that medications play a major role in these premature deaths. We need to teach people in the mental health field the importance of reducing the emphasis on medication as the *only* tool for helping people in acute emotional distress. We need to develop our understanding that extreme emotional states are great teachers — and not illnesses. Shifting our thinking from a narrow medical model to the empowerment paradigm of development and recovery would help reduce our over-reliance on medication as the primary answer to every mental health issue. We would then create programs and places to help people detox from potentially lethal combinations of psychiatric medications.

Create culture change with recovery dialogues. As people begin to understand and embody heart-to-heart dialogue through eCPR and Open Dialogue, they can influence larger organizational changes through recovery dialogues. When persons with lived experience engage decision-makers in dialogues about recovery, then policies and financing will shift to support dialogical recovery of community. These dialogues can also be carried out publicly through the arts, film, television, and social media. The more people can share their recovery stories, the less fearful the public will be of a community they don't understand. Then recovery programs will receive the support they need, and the stigma associated with lived experience will be diminished.

Nothing about us without us. In Europe, those of us with lived experience are called "experts by experience." We bring the expertise of our lived experience of recovery. Therefore, as called for in the New Freedom Commission Report on Mental Health, we need to spearhead the transformation of the system's approach to recovery of life. Those of us who are experts by experience are implementing this transformation by being meaningfully involved in all aspects of change: from retraining providers and evaluating outcomes, to policy formation, to financial reform, to delivery of community-based services.

Recovery centers and alternatives to hospitalization. Until our industrial communities can become cohesive, we will need to create substitute social networks for those living marginalized lives. Recovery centers and communities run by persons with lived experience are proliferating to fill this need. Many of these centers are also being developed for persons with disabilities and addictions. These centers cover a range of social needs from peer-run respites for persons in crisis to social centers for persons needing a meal or a friend. Presently, when someone is in acute emotional distress and unable to function independently at home, there are few options outside of hospitalization or imprisonment. Not only are institutions more costly than home and community-based alternatives, they are also more traumatic. I predict that those of us with lived experience will continue to develop and expand peer-run alternatives to institutionalization. These will be the recreation of community centers or settlement houses of the past. I also predict that the recreation of community centers will be models for building a better society.

I conclude with confidence that we will have a brighter future. I believe that we are witnessing a transformation of consciousness at a global level, similar to the concept of the "noosphere" described by Pierre Teilhard de Chardin. According to Teilhard, the noosphere is a sphere of consciousness, whose evolution is driven by love. I see the consciousness of the world shifting to encompass a greater respect, acceptance, and understanding of humanity in all its diversity. We are seeing change occurring all over the world. There is a strong movement among people with lived experience to bring hope to people diagnosed with even the most severe conditions, as well as to those not yet diagnosed. Each time one person speaks our truth of recovery, the myth of lifetime disability is dissolved. We are the evidence that people recover. We will not rest as long as we see our brothers and sisters being robbed of hope.

Most of all, my goal in writing this book is to bring hope to everyone with mental health challenges — to those already labeled and those not yet labeled — so that they, too, can live a full and meaningful life within the community. I have been accused of giving people false hope, but I contend that is better than the false hopelessness offered by the present society.

ACKNOWLEDGMENTS

I dedicate this book to everyone who has experienced emotional distress, and to their relatives and friends. As I wrote, I kept the spirits of our movement's early leaders close to my heart—Judi Chamberlin, Rae Unzicker, Sally Zinman, Leonard Frank, Joe Rogers, David Oaks, Celia Brown, and Howie the Harp. I also was inspired by all the people struggling along side me to make the system a more caring place. I dedicate this book to a society that has lost its way and is in need of deeper understanding about how to be human and how to humanely help people who are lost and suffering.

In addition, I want to thank my daughters for encouraging me to write and for urging me to do my own drawings. Thanks to my wife Tish, who has helped me deepen my understanding of myself through her love. I also thank my mother who persistently encouraged me to keep writing. Kim Smith helped me bring my illustrations into a clearer form. I want to acknowledge the editing team of Alan Andre, Anne Weaver, and Frank Gerace. Thank you, Jane Tenenbaum, for layout, proofreading, and encouragement. I want to give a special thanks to Michele Curran, whose final reading of the book helped bring coherence where it had been lacking.

APPENDIX

"Finding Our Voice" Training

"Finding Our Voice" training has three goals: a) the development of the person's individual Voice; b) learning to work collaboratively as a group; c) learning to engage (with one's newly discovered Voice) in dialogue with persons having differing views.

When developing one's individual Voice during training, one experiences stages of connecting personally to one's Self and to the group. This involves transforming anger into passion and finding one's purpose. For many peers, these skills have not been well developed; some, who had once been trapped in monologue, may need to develop the skills necessary to negotiate with others. During training, participants are taught essential skills for engaging in and facilitating dialogue, so that they learn to collaborate in a group. They finish by working together to develop a plan, after which each person makes a presentation to the group. Below are twelve principles of empowerment that are the core of the "Finding Our Voice" Training.

Principle One: Peer Support

The first step in "Finding Our Voice" training is to connect participants with one another on a personal level. This is the essence of peer support. Instinctively, the consumer/survivor movement has learned how vitally important peer support can be. By sharing our deepest truth with others, we foster our personal and collective evolution by awakening to our completeness as human beings.

We evolve in relation to other people. By giving and receiving, sharing and trusting, we become more empowered and aware of interpersonal dynamics. We learn that our most important development comes through relationships of mutual trust and understanding. Just as we can only know ourselves in relationships with others, so, too, we can only find our Voice by engaging in dialogue with others. Perhaps the hardest lesson of dialogue is learning the value of opening one's mind to another's beliefs. This is crucial for defining one's own Voice: we can more readily construct our own point of view after considering a variety of possibilities. Acceptance of another's views requires a bit of internal security; it is not unusual for people to be afraid that their point of view will be taken over by another's perspective. I can clearly recall feeling that way while I was growing up. I had great difficulties with intimacy because I was concerned that a girlfriend would run my life and I was afraid that I would not be able to voice my opinion. Once I developed my own Voice, however, I was no longer afraid of intimacy.

Principle Two: Principles of Recovery of Life

From the start of our meetings for the New Freedom Commission on Mental Health in 2002, I was sure that I wanted "recovery of life" and "self-determination" to be among the overarching goals infused into every part of the commission's final recommendations. I considered myself to be an expert on recovery and I knew from my work that consumer/survivors and their families were inspired by the concept of recovery.

In addition, I realized that recovery could also serve as a unifying theme for the commission since the field of mental health was already greatly fractured by differing agendas. Being against something about which there is no agreement, such as the use of forced treatment, is a far more difficult way to unify people. Often it is more useful to advocate for alternative approaches that lead to recovery, rather than to denounce something like forced treatment in general.

Of all the principles underlying recovery, those of us with lived experience of mental health issues think that self-determination is the most important. In the commission's summary paper, we laid out a plan for transforming the mental health system to a recovery-based system through the application of self-determination at both the individual and the group level. I pushed the commission to summarize our recommendations in the form of a vision statement, with goals and objectives. The vision statement begins, "We see a future when everyone with a mental illness will recover." Among the commission's principles is the statement: "Recovery is about coping with life's issues, not merely symptom reduction." The second goal of the commission's report is: "There will be a recovery-based, consumer- and family-driven system." These principles are the most enduring legacy of the commission's report, and it is clear that they have had a positive influence in advocacy efforts across the country.

Principle Three: A Positive Attitude and Belief in Oneself

Having a positive view of the world can be infectious. With a positive attitude, you become a force that is difficult to stop. Your attitude rubs off on others whether they want it to or not. Although many who sat on the New Freedom Commission would not support the concept of recovery publicly, privately they had trouble countering my enthusiasm for it. They found they could relate to the hopefulness of its concept. One member shared his story of a relative who suffered a form of mental illness, and how much they wished their family member could adopt some of the hopeful approaches that I advocated.

I believe that we are able to achieve what we are able to visualize. We are less likely to achieve goals that we cannot envision ourselves achieving. Often, during the commission meetings, I would look around the room and counter negativity by reciting to myself a line from George Bernard Shaw's play *Back to Methuselah*:

> *I hear you say "Why?" Always "Why?" You see things; and you say "Why?" But I dream things that never were; and I say "Why not?"*

I refused to believe that things must always remain as they are. Martin Luther King Jr. epitomized that view when he gave his "I Have a Dream" speech at the March on Washington in 1963. I kept repeating my own version of his speech to myself, **"I have a dream that one day every person labeled with mental illness will recover and lead a full, respected life in the community."** One of the most frequently cited factors in peoples' recovery is the presence in their life of someone who believed in them. This helps you believe in yourself and in your principles. Then they are more likely to become a reality.

Principle Four: Transforming Reactive Anger Into Passionate Advocacy

Perhaps the greatest damage of trauma is its interference with expressing our deepest Voice and building a true Self. When we are unable to build our true Self and find our inner Voice, we experience a welling up of suppressed anger and/or fear. This anger can suddenly appear in a reactive manner that impedes successful advocacy. Often when a consumer/survivor participates in a board meeting or testifies before a decision-making body, they are either silent due to fear or they flare out with anger that disqualifies their testimony. We effective consumer/survivor leaders work on deepening our own awareness and gaining an appreciation of the source of our anger. We come to realize that our anger is rooted in feelings of righteous indignation prompted by hurtful or humiliating past experiences when our Voice was invalidated. In our "Finding Our Voice" program, we pay close attention to this issue in an effort to help participants become aware of their anger and learn to use it strategically to affect positive change in their community.

Two advocates from Alaska observed, "Angry is something to use — not something to be." In this manner, the energy and the outrage behind the anger is not suppressed but is transformed into constructive passion, which can then serve to motivate effective action. It is our belief that using anger constructively may be our greatest challenge as mental health advocates. On an individual or group basis, expressions of anger are important motivators for changing awareness and in guiding a constructive conversation. Skilled advocates learn to be very adept at using anger to achieve their goals.

In many ways, our difficulty with anger stems from what it means to be labeled mentally ill. In this regard, it is useful to look at the origin of the term mental illness. Before medical descriptions of mental illness existed, other words defined the conditions we now label mental illness. Perhaps the most revealing is the term "madness." In English, the word "mad" has at least two meanings. For those of us who have been labeled mentally ill, we are considered in less clinical circles as being mad, i.e., crazy. We were at times called madmen. But if you have not been labeled a crazy person, being described as mad can mean you are angry. Normal people get mad and they are not diagnosed; they are listened to.

A peer of ours captured this distinction very well. She said she worked within a department of mental health and noticed that her colleagues were frequently getting angry at each other and about their work. When they expressed their anger there was no clamping down on their behavior. In fact, for them it seemed the norm. However, when *she* expressed her anger, there were stern looks of censure. Her unlabeled colleagues would inquire in patronizing tones, "Are you feeling all right?" or "Perhaps you are having a breakdown?" or "It might be a good idea to see if you need more medication."

Thus, there are two very different uses of anger and of attitudes towards persons who express anger. People who have not been labeled can express anger as a day-to-day part of their life without being told that they must not be feeling well. There are also exceptions, which reveal these semantic shifts. For instance, women are not given as much freedom in their expression of anger as men. In fact, women who express anger too frequently or too loudly are given the label of b***h. And in mental health circles, people who express anger are given another B label: borderline. In fact, supervisors frequently told me during my training that the best way to know that you were dealing with a borderline personality (invariably a woman) was whether they made you feel angry.

Anger is nearly always closely related to issues of power, whether the circumstances are professional or personal. Peer support becomes invaluable due to the opportunity to freely express our anger in a situation where power is more equalized. In the mental health world, nearly all other relationships involve a power imbalance, where consumer/survivors hold the position of lower power. As in the rest of the world, it is usually risky to express anger in a relationship where you have less power. Yet the expression of anger can often lead to a way to gain power. In the following sidebar, a variety of consumer/survivors express how they have used anger.

What do experienced advocates say about the use of anger?

When speaking to a group, one should listen very carefully and openly to the thought patterns, prejudices, and emotions of those whom one is addressing. One needs to understand their point of view. Then it becomes possible to effectively use the entire palette of emotions — ranging from anger to compassion. In this respect, the amounts used of any particular emotion are a critical part of the dance between the advocates and the people they are addressing.

We have done this successfully with the Alaska legislature. In the process of addressing possible political change, we used anger at some of the stigmas in our culture to motivate legislators in helping us bring about incremental change. — Advocacy couple

I have let my anger motivate me to gain more knowledge so that I can speak with a clear voice, firmly and calmly. Words sometimes have more meaning when put on paper; I do this to adjust my thoughts so they are not so demonstrably angry. — Female advocate

In the beginning of my recovery, my anger was more frustration and hopelessness. With professionals, I could not find anyone that would listen to what I was saying. If I didn't follow their agenda, they didn't want to work with me. I think the break was finding someone who would work with me.

Now that I am recovered, I use my anger — which I continue to feel is more frustration than anything — as a tool to power my desire to help others along in recovery. I cannot stay angry and stay healthy. Anger leads to negativity and bitterness.— Female advocate

Anger crops up when I begin to take the actions or lack of actions of others personally. I have a fairly sophisticated filtration system, but occasionally anger tilts toward rage. I begin writing poison pen emails, make phone calls, and otherwise lessen my short and long term effectiveness as an advocate. I believe that I can be effective on the lower end of the anger scale.

My anger is usually suppressed. That leaves frustration. This may take a toll on me, but provides a better position to deliver a message. When I remain angry, I get all twitchy and it is sort of ugly. The suppression method was learned early from family.

Psychology and Effective Behavior by James C. Coleman has a relevant passage: "In many situations anger and hostility are normal reactions that may lead to constructive action. Anger and hostility aroused by autocratic and unjust treatment of oneself or others may be used constructively in working for social reforms." — Male advocate

According to the Buddha, "Holding onto anger is like picking up a burning coal to throw at the object of my anger all the while deeply burning myself."

"I am powerless over the thoughts, words, and actions of others. I am responsible for the focus of my thoughts, words, and deeds.

"Feeling anger informs me that I have been unfair to myself or another person has spoken or acted in a way that I perceive is unfair." — Female advocate

When I am part of an advocacy group, and we are able to achieve even a modest goal, I feel some of the anger seep out of me. — Female advocate

Thoughts and reflections about the effective use of anger from experienced advocates suggest the following conclusions:

- Raw anger interferes with advocacy.
- Anger is a healthy reaction; it reflects a passionate desire to effect positive change to get our needs met.
- Understanding and expressing one's anger and frustration ahead of time can facilitate and help motivate for social change.
- Anger is most effective when we feel we can *use* it rather than *be* it.
- Being part of an advocacy group gives individuals more power, which itself decreases frustration and anger.
- Advocacy is much more important when practiced as part of a group because the cohesion of the group allows one to transform anger to passion more readily; one can effect greater change when one is part of a group, which also further reduces anger and frustration.
- If we let anger fester, it eats away at us and destroys our ability to positively contribute to developing a cooperative and cohesive community.

Drawing on the developmental model, we can consider the progression of an advocate as learning and accepting the wisdom that "angry is something to use — not something to be." To me, this has meant developing a greater sense of who I am. In my early years of advocacy, I felt my anger so intensely that there was little opportunity to observe either my own reactions to the anger or others' reactions. I would be dismissed as overly biased towards consumers, leaving no room for any middle ground.

Principle Five: Purpose

Clarifying our purpose and finding meaning adds direction to our lives and focus to our actions. It seems we are all cast upon this earth without a sense of purpose. Gaining a sense of purpose addresses the fundamental, meaningful questions that underlie much of the distress called mental illness. Many of us have had to find a purpose to invest in and direct our lives, rather than passively or actively seeking an exit. Empowerment is about finding purpose because it empowers our life. When we find others who share our purpose, this strengthens our resolve and deepens its power.

For many of us, the consumer movement with its attention to big issues has given our lives meaning and purpose. Our shared purpose then reinforces our passion and our connection with other people. Purpose also becomes infectious. When others who are seeking a purpose sense it in the eyes of those around them, they want to be a part of it. The more broadly we can share our purpose, the stronger we become on both the individual and group level. Purpose has two major elements:

Dreams and vision. Whether we are aware of it or not, we live through our dreams and visions. Native Americans called this their "vision quest;" the American mythologist, writer, and lecturer Joseph Campbell simply described it as "following your bliss." My vision quest came at a time of severe distress. As I felt my life force fading from me in seclusion in a psychiatric hospital, I conceived that I would become a psychiatrist and humanize the mental health system. That dream has guided me ever since.

Concrete steps with time for reflection and feedback. Dreams without action languish and die, just as actions without dreams are unsustainable. Even small steps towards realizing a dream are essential. I started by sharing my dream with my friends, family, and therapist. I then started medical school, taking one course at a time until I felt confident enough to take on a full course load. Reflecting helps us to become aware of whether our actions are true to our dreams and whether they are the most effective means of realizing our goal. Feedback from trusted allies and fellow advocates helped strengthen my resolve.

Principle Six: Practical Prioritized Advocacy Plan

If one is going to change existing policies, it is best to be well prepared. The creation of a concise, prioritized plan of action is essential since principles without plans are shelved and collect dust. The proposed plan needs to have clearly delineated, doable steps. The plan must be clearly written and in a format that all can understand. All consumer/ survivor advocates should be able to articulate the principles upon which the plan is based.

When working on recommendations for the New Freedom Commission's summary, we used an easy-to-remember acronym to describe a recovery-based, consumer-driven "STEPs to recovery" plan. **STEPs** stands for the following elements: **S**ervices and supports; **T**raining and education; **E**valuation and quality assurance; and **P**lanning and policy development.

Never settle for piecemeal planning. Always keep the big picture in mind. All major elements of the system have to change for a genuine transformation to take place. Therefore, take every possible opportunity to speak about and distribute a version of your big plan in a concise format everyone can understand. Prioritizing is a very important aspect of any plan. Policy must be placed first — despite being last in STEP — because, without changes at the decision making level, no sustained change will take place, only appeasement. Policy changes unlock thinking and attitudes and reverse oppressive practices. Policy changes give validity and credibility to every consumer-led change to follow. For example, the New Freedom Commission's recommendations have helped advocates to shift the Veterans Administration, the American Psychological Association, and the Joint Commission on Accreditation towards the recovery approach. Policy changes also mean shifting funding to support changes. It is useful to use numbered lists to stay organized and ensure that all points are addressed. These are easier to remember in the heat of struggle.

Principle Seven: Persistence, Perseverance, and Patience

Sally Zinman is a prime example of the power of persistence and perseverance. She has worked tirelessly and persistently for a coercion-free mental health system in California. Though there have been some setbacks toward reaching this goal, Zinman has won respect from friend and foe alike. The Commissioner of the Department of Mental Health for California once told me how much he admired her advocacy, even when he did not fully agree with it. However, when I advocated that Sally's group's budget be increased, he said he could not increase their budget because they were already very effective with the small budget they had.

In my own case, I had to persist to get recovery incorporated into the vision statement of the New Freedom Commission's report. In addition to the strategies already mentioned, I persisted until the final editing and writing of the report. It's essential to read every draft of a proposed document because some people in powerful positions have learned that it's possible to reverse proposed reforms at the last minute. Keep advocating for what you believe in until the very end. Insist on having the right of final review of any document you help prepare.

Principle Eight: Presence — Through Pride, Poise, and Politeness

I never missed a meeting of the New Freedom Commission, public or private. This was not based on paranoia, but on good common sense. I knew there were many members who wanted to undo the principles that I and other consumers, had worked hard to infuse into the report. They just couldn't do it as easily when I was there.

Presence: In addition to being present, it is important to develop a "presence." By presence we mean the need to be socially visible; that people stand up and take notice when you walk in a room. People sense that you are person of character, infused with self-confidence, and someone they cannot easily push around. Having presence is the opposite of being invisible. Those of us labeled with mental illness have often experienced the painful feeling of being invisible. A similar invisibility among blacks was captured eloquently by Ralph Ellison in his novel *Invisible Man*. Ellison described the need to be in a room with hundreds of light bulbs to counter his feeling of invisibility.

Pride: An essential element of presence, pride is an internal feeling of accomplishment and security, which can manifest itself in a variety of ways. One's posture is an outward manifestation of pride. The more upright and straight-backed the better. Though we can enumerate a number of traits involved in presence, there is an elusive, more emergent quality, which may be the most important. We suspect it has to do with the summation of many of the other **P**s described in this section. Certainly people who are passionate have more presence. Yet presence also amplifies passion. People who have power have presence and, in addition, presence augments power. Persistence enhances presence and yet the opposite is also true. People who are positive are often more present. Purpose also plays a big role. When confronted with a person with a deeply felt purpose we feel their presence more deeply. These are people with strongly held principles and convictions. Presence comes through in many nonverbal aspects such as expression, the spark in one's eye, a spring in one's step, uprightness to one's posture, and strength in one's voice. An ability to connect with others is also vital to presence. Being attentive to the details of the process and showing that you are attending to every remark, keeps the others more honest.

Poise and Politeness: Beyond manners, these factors are the outward expression of an inner centeredness and peace. When you can achieve this state it means you will be able to sustain a point of view with greater resolve and be able to communicate it clearly. Poise is a way of being such that you and the others around you realize you will not be easily swayed from your position because you have already put much thought into it. When you are poised, you gain more respect and are taken more seriously. Politeness is a way of seeing an approach to another person when none seemed apparent. You can disarm them with your charm through a polite approach. A polite approach finds common ground and peace, rather than conflict and rage.

Principle Nine: Persuasion

The essential elements behind the art of persuasion have changed little since the classical world, where it was highly valued in the practice of rhetoric. Rhetoric and persuasion were key parts of the Western tradition's formal liberal arts education and the foundation for civic discourse. However, while the principles of effective persuasion have largely remained unchanged for two millennia, those allowed to practice its art — to inspire and change the world — are no longer limited by their social standing. In ancient Rome, mastering the art of rhetoric and persuasion was restricted to those who were free citizens. Some clever slaves living in Rome were taught practical arts such as mathematics or engineering, but slaves were forbidden to learn history, literature, philosophy, and rhetoric because it was believed that giving the essential tools of persuasion to the powerless could inspire others, and ultimately result in social unrest and disorder. Only the free citizens of Rome — those who maintained power — were allowed to learn how to persuade others.

I see a parallel between ancient Rome's restrictions on education in the liberal arts (from the Latin meaning "free man's arts") and the restriction of information shared with mental health consumer/ survivors. Those in power, whether free citizens or designated professionals, usually want to be the ones possessing the language and the training to persuade others.

Luckily today, with training and practice, the art of persuasion is accessible to anyone who can master it. The late Vermont mental health advocate Linda Corey has observed that among the most effective persuasive tools at her disposal are effectively rendered personal stories. She notes that it is difficult to dismiss or forget a personal story, especially when it is told directly by the person who experienced it. When one can observe another's face, hear the pain in their voice, or sense their happiness or pride of accomplishment, the emotional impact can be monumental. Reading or hearing the same story second-hand is far less persuasive, and its impact seldom lasts as long. Research by Patrick Corrigan validates this observation.

Principle Ten: Public Presenting

Learning the art of effectively presenting yourself and your ideas to others is a vital aspect of individual and collective empowerment. Many people who believed they heard voices during their experience of mental distress have recounted that their recovery was greatly abetted when they acquired their own inner life Voice. As I have previously defined it, this means an ability to express one's views and positions effectively among friends, family, and those at work. This doesn't mean one must feel compelled to speak in public; there are many other ways to express one's Voice and make a contribution.

In general, a mental illness label makes it harder for our words to be believed by others. So we need to appear and be as credible as possible. I was personally terrified of public speaking as a child. My knees literally shook when I spoke in front of a crowd. I overcame these fears by adopting a cause I felt strongly about. Now I believe I speak not only for myself, but for millions of voiceless persons in the system. As Linda Corey observed, "To not speak out publicly keeps your ideas narrowed down. Public speaking builds allies and support."

When addressing a public audience, speak from your heart to your audience's heart. Find the message in your heart you want to communicate and use your passion. Here are twelve valuable items I keep in mind when speaking in public:

1. Know your audience. Think about the best way to reach them. What should you wear? How many slides and charts and graphs will they need? It is best to speak clearly and directly to your audience and about things with which they are already somewhat familiar. Professionals frequently want slides with charts and graphs; I often start with some of those and then pose questions. With consumer/survivors I can start with a conversation and just add the slides when they seem to need them for verification.

2. Look at the location ahead of time. If it is a hospital or clinical setting, take a friend. Walk around in it, as it might trigger traumatic memories.

3. Prepare by considering your most important points and writing them down. At first you might want to write out your whole talk and rehearse it. In time, you may get more comfortable with presenting from your heart. Heart-based presentations can more directly reach the deeper selves of your audience. Do what feels comfortable.

4. The fewer objects between you and your audience the better. Lecterns, podiums, and desks tend to interfere with human connection. I like to be able to move around freely, so a mobile microphone is better. A human connection is important to facilitate trust.

5. Use overheads and Power Points judiciously. Both can be useful as an adjunct to a verbal description, but overuse and redundancy can detract from the personal side of your presentation. Avoid "death by PowerPoint." There is a 5/10/20 rule with PowerPoint: five slides, for ten minutes, at 20-point font size. Easels with large paper pads or whiteboards are useful because people see their words up in front of the group. Easels and white boards are preferable to slides and overheads when presenting to a small group (fewer than twenty-five people).

6. Seek feedback about your presentation. Listen to constructive criticism. We learn to improve through feedback. Ask the participants to fill out evaluation forms.

7. Share, with emotional expression, as much about your personal recovery as possible. Do not overemphasize too many traumatic elements, as these may trigger reactions among the audience or cause you to lose their sympathy in other ways. Telling a part of your personal story of recovery with passion and emotion reaches audiences at a deeper level. Maya Angelou said, "I have learned that people will forget what you said, people will forget what you did, but people will never forget how you made them feel."

8. Learn about the local culture and interests. Find out about your audience's passions — such as their football team — or about the important local sites.

9. Engage the audience in dialogue and conversation. Doing so reduces the formality of the setting and works as a bridge between you and your audience. Asking questions is a good way to get a conversation going. For example: "What does recovery mean to you?"

10. You can catch more flies with honey than with vinegar. Think of areas where you can assist your audience. Try to help make their work more meaningful and their life more positive. Hope and recovery often are the types of positive messages most people feel good about.

11. Avoid ranting about one topic or one point of view. Try not to alienate your audience by focusing on topics that prompt a strong negative reaction. Be aware of topics that push buttons in you or your audience. Steer the conversation away from such topics by saying, "Personally, I am uncomfortable with..." and "You might consider the alternatives to..." For example, several years ago I reacted too strongly to a group of nurses in Canada. They wanted me to discuss a coercive form of therapy. I was angry, it showed, and I lost my connection with them. I try to use the principle of dialogue focused on suspending my own beliefs sufficiently to hear others.

12. Weave in humor wherever possible. These are difficult issues and can prompt a great deal of stress. Find something that everyone can laugh about, without the humor coming at anyone's expense or from being overly silly. One person said he likes to laugh because it is difficult to be upset and engage in laughter at the time.

Principle Eleven: Partnering

Two major elements of this principle are the need to partner with other persons with lived experience and the need to partner with people not yet labeled.

Partnering among persons with lived experience is a fundamental step after you gain or find your Voice. In fact, your Voice is greatly amplified by being part of a group. There have been historical difficulties when consumers and survivors have attempted to form groups. Originally there was a split between people who identified themselves as consumers and people who called themselves survivors.

A number of factors helped bridge the divide between the two groups. It has been particularly constructive for both groups to focus on recovery as common ground. In addition, adopting the term "persons with lived experience" has unified both factions. (The specific type of lived experience can be defined separately.) These elements helped our movement to form a national group for the first time, in 2006, under the name National Coalition for Mental Health Recovery (NCMHR).

Partnering between persons with lived experience and people not yet labeled requires representatives from advocacy organizations to learn how to collaborate and at times compromise. People who have been labeled mentally ill are particularly sensitive to any indication that a person without such a label doesn't regard them with respect and dignity. Therefore it is vitally important when forging such partnerships that all participants share some basic values. A good example of such a partnership has been the formation of the National Disability Leadership Alliance (NDLA). The NCMHR was a founding member of the NLDA. The NDLA consists of fifteen national disability groups, all united by the common value of "nothing about us without us." Unlike other disability groups that may be run by professionals or parents, the NDLA consists only of groups run by persons with disabilities.

Principle Twelve: Politics

In a sense, all twelve of the **P**s of empowerment are *really* about politics, because politics is the exercise of power. There is the power of passion, the power of principles, the power of persistence, the power of having a positive attitude, the power of presence, the power of personal connections, the power of planning, the power of purpose, and the power of speaking. All of these can influence decisions and policies. This fits with one definition of power, which holds that power can be measured by the ability to change world around you.

The term empowerment has been important to the consumer/survivor movement because we know that our recovery depends on *us*. Individual recovery depends upon each person advocating for and making decisions that enable her or him to lead a full and meaningful life. Our recovery, as a group, depends on our ability to advocate for policies that enable us to participate fully in society. Many of us in the consumer/survivor movement have gained our individual Voices, but creating a collective voice has been hampered as advocates fail to work together with each other and with allies. It is important for us to learn how to make things happen collectively by working with our allies.

When I was serving on the New Freedom Commission, I wanted the other commission members to be aware that I was representing thousands, if not millions, of other people. I worked to include as much public testimony as possible from persons with lived experience, representing a variety of backgrounds and interests. In addition, while the New Freedom Commission was active, I held hearings at the Alternatives Conference and National Association for Rights Protection and Advocacy (NARPA) Conference. Each of these was recorded and transcribed. In all, there were more than 100 testimonials, and all were sent to the commissioners. I frequently surveyed consumer/survivors and advocates about the work of the commission and, in turn, I would summarize their comments and forward them to the other commissioners. The commission website also had a section for public comment where more than 1,000 comments from consumer/survivors were available for everyone to read.

The politics of power through allies can be supplemented by politics in the form of theatrics. The New Freedom Commission formed a subcommittee on evidence-based practices and I wanted Jean Campbell of the Missouri Institute of Mental Health to have an opportunity to speak. However, the subcommittee's chair declared that the agenda was set and that Jean Campbell would need to take a seat along the wall. The speaker's table was composed of a who's who of the mental health world, including leaders of the American Psychiatric Association and managed care companies. However at the front of the table there was an open chair, and when the chairperson wasn't looking I invited Jean to sit in the chair. When the chairperson came to call on the next person at the table, it was Jean. It would have been an embarrassment to remove her from the table, so she got to speak after all. Find your place at the table through theatre, if necessary!

Politically, it can be important to know the difference between using power within the system and the power of working outside the system. Internal advocates can make a difference in meetings and in documents that are closed to external advocates. Conversely, external advocates are free to say things those within cannot. While a member of the New Freedom Commission, I was aware that one of the commission's ex-officio members was sympathetic to those working for the right to have seclusion and restraint-free environments. I also knew that this individual was not a full member of the commission and, therefore, could not put this recommendation in the report. So, as an internal advocate, I made sure that every version of the report had that language in it. In the end the language was in the report.

BIBLIOGRAPHY

Andersen, T. Human Participating: Human "Being" is the Next Step for Human "Becoming" in the Next Step. In: *Collaborative Therapy*. Anderson, H. and Gehart, D. (Eds.) New York: Routledge, pp. 81–93. 2007.

Bakhtin, M. *Problems of Dostoevsky's Poetics*. Emerson, C. (Ed. and Translator). Minneapolis: U. of Minnesota. 1984.

Barker, P. *Ghost in the Road*. New York: William Abrahams. 1995.

Bateson,G. and Bateson, M.C. *Angels Fear: Towards an Epistemology of the Sacred*. New Jersey: Hampton Press. 2004.

Bentall, R. P. *Reconstructing Schizophrenia*. London: Routledge. 1990.

Bohm,D. *On Dialogue*. London: Routledge Classic. 2004.

Buber, M. *Between Man and Man*. New York: Collier Books. 1965.

Chamberlin, J. *On Our Own*. Lawrence, MA: National Empowerment Center. 2002.

Corrigan, P. W. Changing Stigma through Contact. *Advances in Schizophrenia and Clinical Psychiatry*, 1, pp. 614–625. 2005.

Deci, E. L., and Ryan, R. M. A Motivational Approach to Self: Integration in Personality. In: *Nebraska Symposium on Motivation*. R. Dienstbier (Ed.). *Vol. 38. Perspectives on Motivation*. Lincoln, NE: Univ. of Nebraska Press. pp.237–288. 1991.

Dorman, D. *Dante's Cure*. New York: Other Press. 2003.

Epston, D. and White, M. *Experience, Contradiction, Narrative, and Imagination*. Adelaide, Australia: Dulwich Center Publications. 1992.

Évely, L. *that man is you*. New York: Paulist Press. 1963.

Fisher D. B. Promoting Recovery. In: *Learning About Mental Health Practice*. T. Stickley and T. Basset (Eds.). Chichester, UK: John Wiley & Sons. 2008.

Fisher, D. B., and L. Spiro. Finding and Using Our Voice. In: *Handbook of Mental Health Self-help*. L. Brown (Ed.). New York: Springer Publishing. 2010.

Fisher, D. B., Romprey, D., Filson, B., and Miller, L. *From Relief to Recovery*. Gains Center, New York. 2006.

Freire, P. *Pedagogy of the Oppressed*. New York: Herder and Herder. 1970.

Garety, P. and Freeman, D. Cognitive Approaches to Delusions: A Critical Review of Theories and Evidence. *British Journal of Critical Psychology*. 38:113–154. 1999.

Goffman, I. *Asylums: Essays on the Social Situation of Mental Patients and Other Inmates*. New York: Anchor. 1961.

Harding, C. M., Brooks, G. W., Asolaga, Strauss, J. S., and Breier, A. The Vermont Longitudinal Study of Persons with Severe Mental Illness, I. Methodology, Study Sample, and Overall Status 32 Years Later. *American Journal of Psychiatry*. 144:718–728. 1987.

Harrop, C. and Trower, P. *Why Does Schizophrenia Develop at Late Adolescence?* London: Wiley Press. 2003.

Isaacs, W. *Dialogue and the Art of Thinking Together*. New York: Currency. 1999.

Jablensky, A. and Cole, S. W. Is the Earlier Age of Onset of Schizophrenia in Males a Confounding Variable? *British Journal of Psychiatry*. 170:234–240. 1997.

Jablensky, A., Sartorius, N., Ernberg, G., Anker, M., Korten, A., Cooper, J. E., Day, R., and Bertelsen, A. *Schizophrenia: Manifestations, Incidence and Course in Different Cultures. A World Health Organization Ten-Country Study. Psychological Medicine Monograph Supplement 20.* Cambridge, UK: Cambridge University Press. 1992.

Jablensky, A. and Sartorius, N. What Did the WHO Studies Really Find? *Schizophrenia Bulletin*. 151:253–55. 2008.

Karon, B. and VanDenBos, G. *Psychotherapy of Schizophrenia*. New York: J. Aronson. 1981.

Laing, R. D. *The Divided Self: An Existential Study in Sanity and Madness*. New York: Penguin. 1965.

Louw, D. J. Ubuntu: An African Assessment of the Religious Other. Presented at Annual Meeting of the American Academy of Religion, San Francisco. Nov. 1997. https://www.bu.edu/wcp/Papers/Afri/AfriLouw.htm

Louw, D. J. *Ubuntu and the Challenges of Multiculturalism in Post-apartheid South Africa*. Utrecht, Netherlands: Expertisecentrum Zuidelijk. 2002.

Nasar, S. *A Beautiful Mind*. New York: Simon and Shuster. 1999.

National Empowerment Center, http://www.power2u.org/downloads/SAMHSA%20Recovery%20Statement.pdf. 2006.

Perry, J. W. *Far Side of Madness*. Putnam, Connecticut: Spring Publications. 1974.

Pfeiffer, F. *Meister Eckhart*. (Translated by C. de B. Evans.) London: Watkins.1924.

Read, J. Childhood Adversity and Psychosis. https://www.youtube.com/watch?v=Y6do5bkUEys, 2013.

Seikkula, J., Aaltonen, J., Alakare, B., Haarakangas, K., Nen, J. K., Lehtinen, K. Five-year Experience of First-episode Nonaffective Psychosis in Open-dialogue Approach: Treatment Principles, Follow-up Outcomes, and Two Case Studies. *Psychotherapy Research*. 16: 214–228, 2006.

Seikkula, J. and Olson, M. E. The Open Dialogue Approach to Acute Psychosis: its Poetics and Micropolitics. *Family Process*. 42:403–18, 2003.

Seikkula, J. and Trimble, D. Healing Elements of Therapeutic Conversation: Dialogue as an Embodiment of Love. *Family Process*. 44: 461–475. 2005.

Stern, D. N. *The Present Moment in Psychotherapy and Everyday Life*. New York: W. W. Norton. 2004.

Tiedens, L. Z. Anger and Advancement Versus Sadness and Subjugation: The Effect of Negative Emotion Expressions on Social Status Conferral. *Journal of Personality and Social Psychology*. 80:86–94. 2001.

Teilhard de Chardin, P. *Phenomenon of Man*. New York: Harper Collins. 1959.

Trevarthen, C. Action and Emotion in Development of the Human Self, Its Sociability and Cultural Intelligence: Why Infants Have Feelings Like Ours. In: J. Nadel and D. Muir (Eds.) *Emotional Development*. Oxford: Oxford University Press. pp. 61–91. 2005.

Wunderink, L., Nieboer, R. M., Wiersma, D., Sytema, S., and Nienhuis, F. J. Recovery in Remitted First-episode Psychosis at 7 Years of Follow-up of an Early Dose Reduction/discontinuation or Maintenance Treatment Strategy: Long-term Follow-up of a 2-year Randomized Clinical Trial. *JAMA Psychiatry*. 70:913–20. 2013.

damefisher@
gmail.com

Nec